NEW National Curriculum Mathematics

27/02

M. J. Tipler
K. M. Vickers

Target Book 2

Stanley Thornes (Publishers) Ltd

First published in 1998 by
Stanley Thornes (Publishers) Ltd
Ellenborough House
Wellington Street
CHELTENHAM
GL50 1YW

A catalogue record of this book is available from the British Library

ISBN 0 7487 3547 X

98 99 00 01 02 / 10 9 8 7 6 5 4 3 2 1

The publishers are grateful to the following for permission to
reproduce photographs:

Britstock–IFA: p.1
Martyn Chillmaid: pp. 36, 65, 173
Sylvia Corda Photolibrary: p.111

Typeset and Illustrated by Hardlines, Charlbury, Oxford
Printed and bound in Spain by Mateu Cromo

Contents

Preface

Welcome to Target Book 2. We know you will enjoy working with it. You can learn maths by doing it.

In this book, there are lots of clear examples to show you what to do and then lots of ways to practise.

This book is full of interesting and exciting activities to help you understand and enjoy maths.

Exercises – these are graded so the easy ones come first.

Investigations – these have things for you to discover.

Tasks – these have things for you to do.

Games – these are an interesting way for you to practise your skills.

Puzzles – try and solve these.

Each chapter has Homework/Reviews that your teacher may give you for homework or in class. They are for you to practise what you have learnt in the last few pages.

At the end of each chapter there is a Chapter Review. This is like a chapter test to see what you have remembered. Your teacher may give it to you at the end of the chapter or at some other time during the year.

If you see , this means that you will need a calculator for the exercise.

If you see , this means that are not allowed to use a calculator for the exercise.

Maths is all around you. It will be part of whatever you choose to do when you leave school. Target Books 1–5 will give you a good maths education up to GCSE.

Best wishes for an enjoyable and successful year in maths.

M J Tipler
K M Vickers

1 Numbers

Behind bars...................

People who go to jail are given a number.

Who else is given a number? Why?

COUNTY JAIL

003-954700214

Place value

Remember . . .

234 is 2 hundreds and 3 tens and 4 ones.

234 can be shown as

2 hundreds   3 tens   4 ones

999 can be shown as

9 hundreds   9 tens   9 ones

What happens to 999 if we add another one?

1286 is 1 thousand, 2 hundreds, 8 tens and 6 ones.

1286 can be shown as

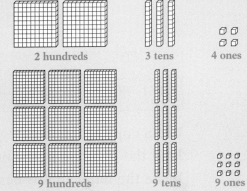

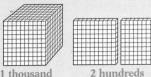

1 thousand   2 hundreds   8 tens

6 ones

0, 1, 2, 3, 4, 5, 6, 7, 8 and 9 are sometimes called digits.

Exercise 1   **A**   What is the tens digit in these?

1. 78	2. 60	3. 582	4. 763
5. 308	6. 1324	7. 6832	8. 5140
9. 7050	10. 6304	11. 7200	

B   What is the hundreds digit in these?

1. 473	2. 560	3. 408	4. 4325
5. 7960	6. 5070	7. 6009	

C   What is the thousands digit in these?

1. 5863	2. 4721	3. 3840	4. 5064
5. 3080	6. 6004	7. 3270	

Example   5 thousands, 4 hundreds, 2 tens and 8 ones is written as 5428.
6 thousands, 4 tens and 3 ones is written as 6043.
3 thousands and 2 ones is written as 3002.

Exercise 2   **What does a lion eat when he goes out to tea?**

		E					E	
6401	4080	5432	4008	6148	8016	6401	5432	4681

Use a copy of this box.

Find the number, in the box, that fits the words below.

Write the letter that is beside the words on the line above the answer.

The first one has been done.

E   5 thousands, 4 hundreds, 3 tens and 2 ones

A   6 thousands, 1 hundred, 4 tens and 8 ones

R   4 thousands, 6 hundreds, 8 tens and 1 one

I   8 thousands, 1 ten and 6 ones

H   4 thousands and 8 tens

T   6 thousands, 4 hundreds and 1 one

W   4 thousands and 8 ones

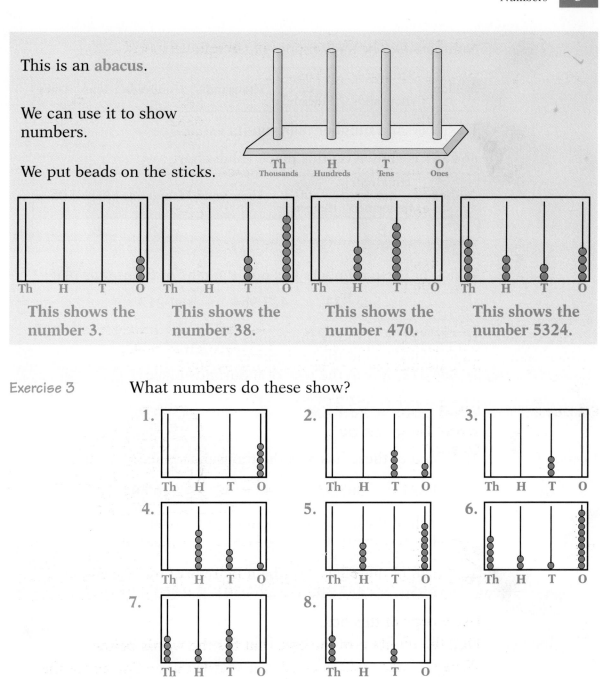

This is an abacus.

We can use it to show numbers.

We put beads on the sticks.

Th Thousands   H Hundreds   T Tens   O Ones

This shows the number 3.

This shows the number 38.

This shows the number 470.

This shows the number 5324.

Exercise 3   What numbers do these show?

1.   Th H T O

2.   Th H T O

3.   Th H T O

4.   Th H T O

5.   Th H T O

6.   Th H T O

7.   Th H T O

8.   Th H T O

Exercise 4   Jan has 4 beads.

She made the number 13 on the abacus.

What other numbers could she make using 4 beads?

Write as many as you can.

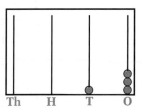

Th H T O

Numbers can be shown on a **place value chart**.

Millions	Hundreds of thousands	Tens of thousands	Thousands	Hundreds	Tens	Ones

The **place** of a number tells you its **value**.

864 381 is shown on this place value chart.

Millions	Hundreds of thousands	Tens of thousands	Thousands	Hundreds	Tens	Ones
	8	6	4	3	8	1

Example   Which of these numbers has 6 in the tens of thousands place?

$$586\ 321 \qquad 427\ 964 \qquad 364\ 213$$

Answer   In 586 321, 6 is in the thousands place.
In 427 964, 6 is in the tens place.
In 364 213, 6 is in the tens of thousands place.

The answer is 364 213.

Exercise 5

1. Which of these has 8 in the thousands place?

   384 321   865 932   428 172   916 842

2. Which of these has 5 in the tens of thousands place?
   384 259   596 401   657 814   685 000

3. Which of these has 4 in the hundreds of thousands place?
   347 986   487 300   264 501   863 420

Example   In £48 725 the place value of the 4 is tens of thousands.

Exercise 6

What is the place value of the 4 in these?

1. £846
2. £472
3. £704
4. £5431
5. £4320
6. £7004
7. £8640
8. £13 304
9. £14 852
10. £41 652
11. £28 467
12. £384 962
13. £482 721
14. £342 652

Reading and writing numbers

Thousands

8	5	4	7	3	2

To read 854 732 we read in lots of 3.

The last 3 numbers are 732.
We read these as seven hundred and thirty two.

The first 3 numbers, 854, are the thousands.
We read these as eight hundred and fifty four thousand.

So 854 732 is read as eight hundred and fifty four thousand,
seven hundred and thirty two.

Examples 6725 is read as six thousand, seven hundred and twenty five.

72 432 is read as seventy two thousand, four hundred and
thirty two.

564 837 is read as five hundred and sixty four thousand, eight
hundred and thirty seven.

Exercise 7 **A** Write these in words.

1.	96	2.	52	3.	387	4.	652
5.	3000	6.	5360	7.	7291	8.	4034
9.	5009	10.	6008	11.	3050	12.	36 852
13.	50 480	14.	30 039	15.	63 009	16.	532 471
17.	504 601	18.	700 301	19.	509 004		

B Write the amount on these cheques in words.

1. STANLEYS BANK Date 8th Jan 1999
Pay Mr Tom £ 526
J P Young

STANLEYS BANK Date 8th Jan 1998
Pay Mr Brown £ 4680
K M Catley

3. STANLEYS BANK Date 5th Feb 2001
Pay Mrs Maths £ 32 741
C Langham

STANLEYS BANK Date 5th Feb 2000
Pay Jan Cole £ 84 506
J Jansom

5. STANLEYS BANK Date 1st Sep 1998
Pay Jim Dick £ 326 420
I P Kingsley

STANLEYS BANK Date 1st Sep 2000
Pay Fred Lint £ 804 106
K Small

Exercise 8

Use a copy of this.

Fill it in.

1. across is done for you.

1 **3**	2 **0**	3 **4**	**1**	**0**	■	4	5	6
	■	7		■	8	■	9	
10				■	11	12		
■		13		14	■		■	■
15	■		■	16			17	■
18	19		20		■		21	
■		■	22	23		■	24	
25		26			■	■	27	28
	■		■	29				

Across

1. thirty thousand, four hundred and ten
4. five hundred and sixty four
7. eighty six
9. fifty nine
10. eight thousand and four
11. nine thousand, three hundred
13. five hundred and fifty nine
16. six thousand and seventy nine
18. two thousand, three hundred and two
21. eight hundred and nine
22. ninety seven
24. twenty
25. sixteen thousand, five hundred and five
27. forty eight
29. ninety thousand and seventy three

Down

1. three hundred and eight
2. four hundred and eighty thousand, five hundred
3. one thousand, six hundred and forty five
5. six hundred and fifty
6. four hundred and ninety
8. seventy nine
12. thirty thousand, seven hundred and eighty two
14. ninety six
15. seventy two
17. ninety thousand and forty seven
19. three hundred and forty six
20. two hundred and ninety
23. seven hundred and fifty nine
25. fourteen
26. fifty seven
28. eighty three

Homework/Review 1

A What is the hundreds digit in these?

1. 864   **2.** 5325
3. 7896   **4.** 5004

B **When is a gun out of work?**
Use a copy of this box.

		E				
___	___	___	___		___	___
3560	6205	6034	3056		3526	6253

				E	
___	___	___	___	___	___
3526	6025	6050	3526	6005	6034 3506

E 6 thousands, 3 tens and 4 ones

I 3 thousands, 5 hundreds, 2 tens and 6 ones

D 3 thousands, 5 hundreds and 6 ones

S 6 thousands, 2 tens and 5 ones

N 3 thousands, 5 tens and 6 ones

H 6 thousands, 2 hundreds and 5 ones

W 3 thousands, 5 hundreds and 6 tens

R 6 thousands and 5 ones

T 6 thousands, 2 hundreds, 5 tens and 3 ones

F 6 thousands and 5 tens

C What is the place value of 8 in these?

1. 1864   **2.** 38 324   **3.** 84 627   **4.** 389 652
5. 834 962   **6.** 308 514   **7.** 700 805

D Write these in words.

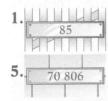
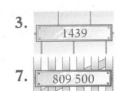
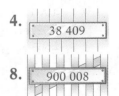

1. 85   **2.** 632   **3.** 1439   **4.** 38 409

5. 70 806   **6.** 340 962   **7.** 809 500   **8.** 900 008

E Write in numbers.

1. five hundred and eighty
2. two thousand, six hundred and four
3. seventy two thousand, six hundred and eighty two
4. eighty thousand, nine hundred and twelve
5. six hundred and fifty two thousand and four hundred

Putting numbers in order

Remember . . .

387 and 378 have the same number of hundreds.

387 has more tens than 378.

So 387 is bigger than 378.

Exercise 9   Which is bigger?

1.	78 or 87	2.	169 or 203	3.	579 or 597
4.	832 or 809	5.	568 or 563		

3864 and 3796 have the same number of thousands.

3864 has more hundreds than 3796.

So 3864 is bigger than 3796.

Which is smaller 3879 or 3897?

Exercise 10   **A** Which is bigger?

1.	1389 or 2176	2.	5364 or 4895	3.	9872 or 9694
4.	3590 or 3604	5.	7304 or 7501	6.	4639 or 4641
7.	6078 or 6071	8.	4905 or 4902		

B Which is smaller?

1.	9862 or 8321	2.	4950 or 4632	3.	2814 or 2841
4.	7906 or 7909	5.	3005 or 3010		

Exercise 11

car A   car B   car C   car D

£8769   £8050   £8771   £8796

1. Which car costs the most?
2. Which car costs the least?

48 is a 2-digit number.

683 is a 3-digit number.

Exercise 12

These are number cards.

1. Sam picked these cards.
    What is the smallest number that
    can be made using Sam's cards?

2. Helen picked these cards.
    What is the smallest 2-digit
    number that can be made
    using Helen's cards?

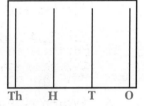

Remember   The **even** numbers are 2, 4, 6, 8, 10, ...
The **odd** numbers are 1, 3, 5, 7, 9, ...

Exercise 13   Ben has 5 beads.
He puts them on the abacus.

1. What is the biggest 2-digit
    number he can make?
2. What is the biggest 3-digit
    number he can make?
3. What is the smallest 2-digit number he can make?
4. What is the smallest 3-digit even number he can make?
5. What is the biggest odd number he can make?

Example   Which is bigger?
38 654 or 38 723

Answer   They both have 38 thousands.
38 723 has more hundreds than 38 654.
So 38 723 is bigger.

Exercise 14

Use a copy of this table.
Which number is bigger?
Shade it on your table. The first one is done.

526	149 003
3 552 202	43 682
5534	3 552 022
486 054	562
194 300	62 009
69 002	496 045
9795	5435

1. 526 or 562
2. 5534 or 5435
3. 62 009 or 69 002
4. 43 682 or 9795
5. 149 003 or 194 300
6. 486 054 or 486 045
7. 3 552 022 or 3 552 202

The shading makes a letter. Which letter?

Remember . . .

To put numbers in order from biggest to smallest, pick the biggest number then the next biggest.

Keep picking the next biggest until there are none left.

To put numbers in order from smallest to biggest, pick the smallest first.

Exercise 15   **A**   Put these in order from biggest to smallest.

    1.   78, 87, 96, 83, 79   **2.**   327, 723, 372, 307, 203
    3.   1879, 1897, 1987, 1789   **4.**   1431, 1354, 1541, 1435
    5.   7989, 7899, 7998, 8997   **6.**   6324, 6342, 6346, 6364
    7.   29 684, 29 692, 28 693, 29 926

B   Put these in order from smallest to biggest.

    1.   56, 65, 79, 61   **2.**   792, 783, 795, 729
    3.   3857, 3850, 3580, 3875   **4.**   4059, 4062, 4039, 4509
    5.   8329, 8923, 8239, 8932

C   £179 642   £179 462   £197 642   £197 462   £179 264

Put these in order from biggest to smallest.

Exercise 16

GUESS HOW MANY

Name	Guess
Jon	1863
Dilys	2427
Rob	1764
Anna	2472
Ravi	1961

    1.   Who guessed the biggest number?
    2.   Who guessed the smallest number?
    3.   Put the 5 numbers in order from smallest to biggest.
    4.   There were 2435 jelly beans in the jar. Who was closest?

Homework/Review 2

A Which is bigger?
1. 364 or 371
2. 279 or 272
3. 6314 or 6413
4. 5872 or 8527
5. 3098 or 3908
6. 7200 or 7020

B
1. Which class collected the most cans?
2. Which class collected the least cans?

Class	Number of cans
8A	1762
8B	1954
8C	1729
8D	1872

C
1. What is the biggest 3-digit number that can be made using these number cards?

2. What is the smallest 4-digit number that can be made?
3. What is the smallest 2-digit even number that can be made?

D Use a copy of this.
Which number is bigger?
Shade it on your table.
1. 627 or 672
2. 4431 or 4341
3. 72 805 or 78 200
4. 53 641 or 9879
5. 348 609 or 348 906
6. 729 063 or 729 036
7. 4 566 941 or 4 569 641
What letter does the shading make?

729 063	672	72 805
348 906	729 036	348 609
4431		627
4 569 641	9879	4 566 941
53 641	78 200	4341

E Put these in order from smallest to biggest.
1. 564, 645, 465, 546
2. 3682, 3862, 3268, 3286
3. 39 407, 39 704, 39 074, 39 047

F
1. Which month were the most cakes sold?
2. Which month were the least cakes sold?
3. Put the number of cakes sold in order from biggest to smallest.

Month	Number of cakes sold
January	38 652
February	27 987
March	39 420
April	38 561
May	27 764
June	39 351

Game for a group: LADDERS

You will need   a ladder like this for each player

To play   • Your teacher will call out 7 numbers between 0 and 20.
The numbers will be called one at a time.

   • As each number is called, put it on the ladder.

   • The numbers must be put on the ladder in order.

Example   Mindu put 18 at the **top** of her ladder.
The teacher then called 19.
Mindu could not put this on her ladder.

   • The winner is the person who has put the most numbers on the ladder.
This person gets 1 point.

   • Play again.
Your teacher will choose numbers between 0 and 50 **or** 100 and 200
or 1000 and 1050 **or** 1000 and 2000 **or** 10 000 and 20 000.

Investigation

Tom made the numbers 547 475 247
using these number cards.

What other 3-digit numbers can Tom make?
Write them all down in order.

Zenta had these cards.

Write down all the 3-digit numbers she could make with them.

Can Zenta make as many as Tom?

Diana had these cards.

How many 3-digit numbers can she make with them?

Can you always make the same number of 3-digit numbers
with 4 cards?

◀◀ CHAPTER REVIEW ◀◀

◀◀
Exercise 1
on page 2

A What is the tens digit in these?
  1. 387   **2.** 5401   **3.** 38 652   **4.** 41 000

◀◀
Exercise 6
on page 4

B What is the place value of the 8 in these?
  1. 78   **2.** 586   **3.** 3842
  4. 58 720   **5.** 800 312

◀◀
Exercise 7
on page 5

C Write these in words.
  1. 364   **2.** 508   **3.** 1862
  4. 38 351   **5.** 600 415   **6.** 780 007

◀◀
Exercise 8
on page 6

D What goes in the gap? The first one is done.
  1.   **2.**   **3.**

| TICKET 3052 | TICKET | TICKET |
| Three thousand and fifty two | Thirteen thousand, five hundred and six | Eleven thousand and seventeen |

◀◀
Exercise 10
on page 8

E Which is smaller?
  1. 9652 or 9781   **2.** 7651 or 7615   **3.** 4320 or 4300

◀◀
Exercise 12
on page 9

F **1.** What is the biggest 4-digit number 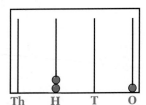 you can make using these?
  2. What is the smallest 3-digit even number you can make?

◀◀
Exercise 14
on page 9

G Which is bigger?
  1. 63 479 or 63 749   **2.** 586 310 or 586 301

◀◀
Exercise 15
on page 10

H Put these in order from smallest to biggest.
  1. 5361, 6135, 5631, 6153
  2. 20 618, 60 218, 20 168, 21 068

◀◀
Exercise 4
on page 3

I Jim has 3 beads.
He made the number 201 on the abacus.
What other numbers could he
make using all 3 beads?
Write as many as you can.

Th   H   T   O

2 Adding and Subtracting

On the road..

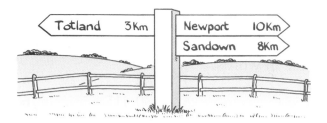

We often have to add or subtract when we drive somewhere.

- What is the distance between Newport and Totland?
- Which other places can you work out the distances between?

Adding and subtracting with numbers up to 20

Remember . . .

You should know the **addition facts** on this table.

+	0	1	2	3	4	5	6	7	8	9	10	11	12	13	14	15	16	17	18	19	20
0	0	1	2	3	4	5	6	7	8	9	10	11	12	13	14	15	16	17	18	19	20
1	1	2	3	4	5	6	7	8	9	10	11	12	13	14	15	16	17	18	19	20	
2	2	3	4	5	6	7	8	9	10	11	12	13	14	15	16	17	18	19	20		
3	3	4	5	6	7	8	9	10	11	12	13	14	15	16	17	18	19	20			
4	4	5	6	7	8	9	10	11	12	13	14	15	16	17	18	19	20				
5	5	6	7	8	9	10	11	12	13	14	15	16	17	18	19	20					
6	6	7	8	9	10	11	12	13	14	15	16	17	18	19	20						
7	7	8	9	10	11	12	13	14	15	16	17	18	19	20							
8	8	9	10	11	12	13	14	15	16	17	18	19	20								
9	9	10	11	12	13	14	15	16	17	18	19	20									
10	10	11	12	13	14	15	16	17	18	19	20										

Exercise 1   Write down the answers to these.

1. 3 + 5   2. 7 − 4   3. 6 + 5
4. 8 + 8   5. 12 − 7   6. 9 + 8
7. 11 − 5   8. 17 − 5   9. 12 + 6
10. 20 − 8   11. 15 − 7   12. 9 + 6
13. 19 − 11   14. 17 − 12   15. 11 + 0
16. 16 − 7   17. 13 + 7

Exercise 2   This is a **number grid**.

The numbers inside the boxes
add to give the numbers in blue.

5	3	8 5+3=8
2	3	5 2+3=5

7   6
5+2=7   3+3=6

Use a copy of this.
Fill in the number grids.

1.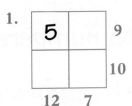

2.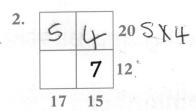

Investigation

How many ways can this be filled in?

		20
		14

18   16

Exercise 3   **A** Write down the answers to these.

1. 5 + 6 + 7   2. 9 + 6 + 5   3. 7 + 8 + 3
4. 11 + 4 + 2   5. 1 + 6 + 8   6. 3 + 0 + 12
7. 9 + 8 + 1   8. 6 + 3 + 9

B Make a copy of this.
Put one of the numbers from
the box in each gap.

9	19	8	11

1. __ + 8 − 3 = 14   2. 7 + __ − 4 = 11
3. __ − 11 + 5 = 13   4. 20 − __ + 5 = 14

Puzzles

Use a copy of this.

1.

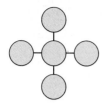

Put the numbers 1 to 5 in the circles.
Each line of circles must add to 8.

Do this again but this time the circles must add to 10.

2.

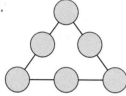

Put the numbers 1 to 6 in the circles.
Each line of circles must add to 10.

Try to put the numbers 1 to 6 in the circles so each line adds to a number other than 10.

Adding and subtracting with numbers up to 99

Remember . . .

```
  56
 +23
  79
```
Add the ones first. $6 + 3 = 9$
Then add the tens. $5 + 2 = 7$

```
  86
 - 34
  52
```
Subtract the ones first. $6 - 4 = 2$
Then subtract the tens. $8 - 3 = 5$

Exercise 4   Use a copy of these. Fill in the answers.

1.
```
  24
 + 3
```

2.
```
  62
 + 5
```

3.
```
  79
 - 8
```

4.
```
  87
 - 7
```

5.
```
  54
 +25
```

6.
```
  39
 - 25
```

7.
```
  87
 - 64
```

Remember . . .

```
  5 4      4 ones + 8 ones is 12 ones.
+3₁8       12 ones is 1 ten and 2 ones.
  9 2      Write down the 2 ones.
           Add the 1 ten to the tens.
           5 tens + 3 tens + 1 ten is 9 tens.
```

```
 ⁶7̷ ¹3     We can't take 8 ones from 3 ones.
 − 2 8     So we make one of the tens into 10 ones.
   4 5     13 ones take away 8 ones is 5 ones.
           6 tens take away 2 tens is 4 tens.
```

Exercise 5 **A** Use a copy of these. Fill in the answers.

1. 38 +26	2. 57 +36	3. 49 +23	4. 54 +17
5. 64 − 18	6. 34 − 17	7. 86 − 57	8. 93 − 78
9. 85 − 79	10. 70 − 36	11. 51 − 29	

B Find the answers to these.

1. 27 + 39   2. 68 + 27   3. 83 − 47   4. 62 − 39
5. 53 − 37   6. 42 + 18   7. 50 − 28   8. 43 − 17

Exercise 6

1. The picture shows how Lena's
   3 hoops landed.
   How many points did she get?

2. Owen threw 4 hoops and got 28 points.
   What numbers go in the gaps?
   Owen threw _____ hoops over the five
   and _____ hoops over the nine.

3. Bethan threw 5 hoops.
   Write down 2 ways she could get
   more than 35 points.

Exercise 7

This is a **number chain**.

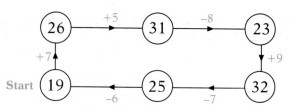

Use a copy of this.

Fill in the missing numbers.

1.
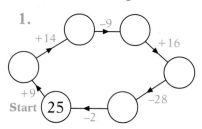

2.
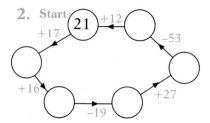

Remember . . .

Magic squares

No matter which way you add
you get the same answer.

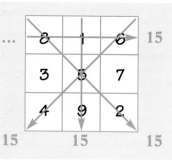

Exercise 8

Use a copy of these magic squares.
Fill in the missing numbers.

1.

29	19	33
21	35	

2.

		17
	32	42
		37

3.

42		
22	30	
		18

Exercise 9

Claire dropped ink on her sums.
What numbers have been covered?

1.

2.

3.

4 8
+ 9
8

Exercise 10

Find the answers to these.

1. fifty seven plus thirty four   2. sixty one minus forty five
3. eighty three minus fifty nine   4. nineteen plus sixty seven
5. ninety five minus eighteen

Adding bigger numbers

Examples

$$134$$
$$+253$$
$$387$$

Add the ones first.
Then the tens.
Then the hundreds.

$$5824$$
$$+3153$$
$$8977$$

Add the ones first.
Then the tens.
Then the hundreds.
Then the thousands.

Exercise 11

Use a copy of these.

Fill in the answers.

1.   236
    +142

2.   583
    +406

3.   560
    +329

4.   461
    +321

5.   784
    +102

6.   1863
    +1132

7.   3406
    +293

8.   5643
    +1344

9.   4651
    +2243

10.   3720
    +6139

11.   2630
    +5164

We can show 154 + 169
like this.

1 5 4
+1 6 9
3 2 3

4 + 9 = 13 ones.
Write down the 3.
Add the 1 ten to the tens.
5 + 6 + 1 = 12 tens.
Write down the 2.
Add the 1 hundred to
the hundreds.
1 + 1 + 1 = 3 hundreds.

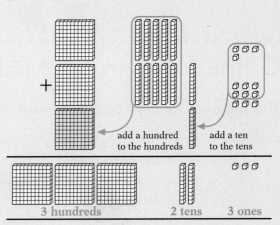

add a hundred
to the hundreds

add a ten
to the tens

3 hundreds   2 tens   3 ones

The answer is 323.

Exercise 12   **A**   Use a copy of this.

Fill in the answers.

1. 387	2. 472	3. 88	4. 57
+ 24	+ 86	+ 96	+ 89

5. 382	6. 683	7. 6583	8. 3134
+159	+274	+ 178	+ 275

9. 795	10. 583	11. 3853	12. 3427
+408	+679	+5129	+5865

B   Find the answers to these.

1. 287 + 316   2. 589 + 64   3. 170 + 86
4. 426 + 208   5. 315 + 217   6. 309 + 248
7. 585 + 346   8. 3835 + 129   9. 4271 + 3596
10. 4387 + 5453   11. 4729 + 2832   12. 5079 + 4034

Exercise 13   ☐ + ☐ = 185

Fill in the boxes to make 185.

Do this 10 different ways.

One way is   140 +   45 = 185.

Game for a group: MAKE IT BIG

You will need a chart like this for each player

To play   • Choose a leader.

• The leader calls out 5 numbers between 0 and 9. The numbers must be called one by one.

• As each number is called, the other players write it in one of their boxes.

• The players then do the addition.

• The player who has made the biggest answer gets a point.

• Play the game 10 times.

• The player with the most points wins.

Example   27 + 36 + 42 + 18 + 136 =

Answer   2 7   7 + 6 + 2 + 8 + 6 = 29 ones.
               3 6   Write down the 9.
               4 2   Add the 2 tens to the tens.
               1 8   2 + 3 + 4 + 1 + 3 + 2 = 15 tens.
            + 1₁ 3₂ 6   Write down the 5.
               2 5 9   Add the 1 to the hundreds.
                            1 + 1 = 2 hundreds.

Exercise 14   Find the answers to these.

1. 12 + 16 + 19   2. 37 + 23 + 51
3. 86 + 52 + 71   4. 39 + 86 + 52 + 47
5. 151 + 86 + 32 + 42   6. 261 + 38 + 53 + 49
7. 87 + 29 + 34 + 26 + 64   8. 33 + 86 + 91 + 142 + 62
9. 78 + 42 + 37 + 463 + 329

Exercise 15   Is this a magic square?

Turn it upside down.

Is it a magic square now?

96	11	89	68
88	69	91	16
61	86	18	99
19	98	66	81

Puzzle

17	27	5	88	64
28	6	48	47	19
66	30		57	33
29	84	69	38	23
14	19	27	38	62

```
   69
   84
   30
   66
 ₂28
  277
```

Use a copy of this.
Start at the blue square.
Draw a path that goes through exactly 5 squares.

You can go or or or

but not

Add up the numbers on your path.

The path shown adds to 277.

Find the path with the biggest answer.

Find the path with the smallest answer.

Homework/Review 1

A Write down the answers to these.
  1. 4 + 5
  2. 7 + 6
  3. 4 + 8
  4. 8 – 3
  5. 16 – 12
  6. 11 – 8
  7. 17 – 4
  8. 9 + 8
  9. 19 – 14
  10. 18 – 7
  11. 20 – 6

B These are magic squares.
Use a copy of them.
Fill in the missing numbers.

1.

6	5	
	6	
5	7	6

2.

4	8	12
		3

C How many burglars can you put into an empty cell?

$\overline{}\ \overline{}\ \overline{}$ $\overset{A}{\overline{}}$ $\overline{}\ \overline{}\ \overline{}\ \overline{}$
923 7444 527 59 8081 160 527 32

$\overline{}\ \overset{A}{\overline{}}\ \overline{}\ \overline{}$ $\overline{}\ \overline{}\ \overline{}$ $\overline{}\ \overline{}\ \overline{}\ \overline{}$
160 197 59 160 160 197 527 43 527 294 294

$\overline{}\ \overline{}\ \overline{}\ \overline{}$ $\overline{}\ \overline{}\ \overline{}\ \overline{}\ \overline{}$
93 322 7444 160 527 29 265 160 518

$\overset{A}{\overline{}}\ \overline{}\ \overline{}\ \overline{}$ $\overline{}\ \overline{}\ \overline{}$
59 7444 518 29 923 32 527

Use a copy of this box.
  A   37 + 22
  R   56 – 24
  C   80 – 37
  I   56 + 37
  M   48 – 19
  T   136 + 24
  S   237 + 85
  F   4687 + 3394

  H   43 + 68 + 72 + 14
  P   83 + 64 + 22 + 96
  Y   73 + 137 + 43 + 265
  L   39 + 54 + 182 + 19
  E   51 + 65 + 84 + 327
  N   4825 + 2619
  O   564 + 359

Subtracting bigger numbers

Examples

```
  587    Subtract the ones first.
- 342    Then the tens.
  245    Then the hundreds.
```

```
  9548   Subtract the ones first.
- 3421   Then the tens.
  6127   Then the hundreds.
         Then the thousands.
```

Exercise 16 Use a copy of these. Fill in the answers.

1. 178
    − 24

2. 583
    − 142

3. 687
    − 304

4. 5709
    − 1509

5. 6497
    − 2384

6. 8641
    − 4320

7. 9986
    − 8352

We can show $\begin{array}{r} 234 \\ -145 \end{array}$ like this.

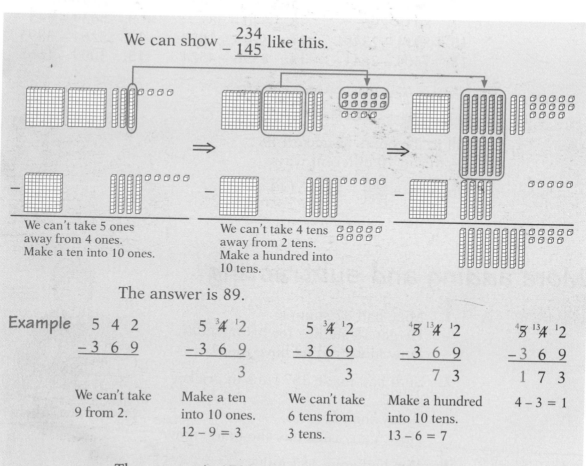

We can't take 5 ones away from 4 ones. Make a ten into 10 ones.

We can't take 4 tens away from 2 tens. Make a hundred into 10 tens.

The answer is 89.

Example

```
  5 4 2
- 3 6 9
```
We can't take 9 from 2.

```
  5 ³4̶ ¹2
- 3 6 9
      3
```
Make a ten into 10 ones.
$12 − 9 = 3$

```
  5 ³4̶ ¹2
- 3 6 9
      3
```
We can't take 6 tens from 3 tens.

```
  ⁴5̶ ¹³4̶ ¹2
-  3 6 9
     7 3
```
Make a hundred into 10 tens.
$13 − 6 = 7$

```
  ⁴5̶ ¹³4̶ ¹2
-  3 6 9
   1 7 3
```
$4 − 3 = 1$

The answer is 173.

Exercise 17   **A**   Use a copy of these.
Fill in the answers.

1. 383 – 274	2. 196 – 179	3. 549 – 352	4. 685 – 394
5. 411 – 264	6. 333 – 266	7. 7480 – 2389	8. 8471 – 6275
9. 9983 – 4697	10. 6736 – 4894	11. 3682 – 1797	

B   Find the answers to these.

1. 782 – 658	2. 321 – 274	3. 582 – 89
4. 564 – 78	5. 451 – 368	6. 279 – 185
7. 803 – 296	8. 540 – 387	9. 5639 – 445
10. 8914 – 2349	11. 3708 – 1889	12. 5264 – 3895
13. 7404 – 3641	14. 8396 – 4524	15. 3009 – 1665

Exercise 18   ☐ – ☐ = 140

Fill in the boxes to make 140.
Do this in 10 different ways.

One way is 200 – 60 = 140.

More adding and subtracting

Exercise 19   **A**   1.   Mike had 87 stamps.
He got 18 stamps for his birthday.
How many did he have then?

2.   Sudi had made 287 runs in cricket
so far.
Today she made 56.
How many runs has she made now?

3.   Ben had gone 187 miles.
He had to go 354 altogether.
How far did he still have to go?

B 1. How many votes did R. Smith get?
2. How many votes did B. Wilson get?
3. Who got the most votes? By how many?
4. How many votes came in on day 1?
5. How many votes came in on day 2?
6. How many more votes came in on day 1 than on day 2?

Name	Votes	
	Day 1	Day 2
R. Smith	3261	2327
B. Wilson	5328	1289

C

Calories			
Food	Calories	Food	Calories
apple	40	cola	135
banana	65	Crisps	156
burger	450	egg	80
CHOC BAR	425	fish	345

How many calories are in these?

1. a burger and a can of cola
2. a chocolate bar and a bag of crisps
3. an apple and a banana
4. a boiled egg and fried fish
5. a burger, a chocolate bar and an apple
6. a chocolate bar, fried fish and a can of cola

Puzzle

1 2 3 4 5 6 7 8 9

⬚⬚ + ⬚⬚ – ⬚ – ⬚⬚⬚ =

Make a copy of this.
Choose any of the numbers above.
Put one number in each box.
Use each number just once.
Make the biggest answer you can.

Homework/Review 2

A   Use a copy of these.

Fill in the answers.

1.	187 − 56	2.	493 − 270	3.	583 − 213	4.	916 − 379

5. 4501
    − 889

6. 6416
    − 3587

7. 7524
    − 3966

B   **How is an eye doctor like a teacher?**

Use a copy of this box.

E   586 − 343 = 243
L   436 − 114
U   589 − 472
H   364 − 248
O   193 − 87
I   465 − 278
S   864 − 379
Y   4226 − 1154
B   5506 − 817
T   9700 − 6992
P   4711 − 1843

```
                 E
___  ___  ___  ___   ___  ___  ___  ___
2708 116  243  3072   4689 106 2708 116
     E                          E
___  ___  ___  ___   ___  ___  ___
2708 243  485  2708   2708 116  243

___  ___  ___  ___  ___  ___
2868 117 2868 187  322  485
```

C

Cans of fruit sold			
	Week 1	Week 2	Week 3
peaches	214	351	186
apples	89	115	172

1.   How many cans of fruit were sold in week 1?
2.   How many were sold in week 2?
3.   Which week were the most cans sold?
4.   How many cans of peaches were sold altogether?
5.   How many more cans of peaches than cans of apples were sold in week 2?

◀◀ CHAPTER REVIEW ◀◀

◀◀
Exercise 1
on page 15

A Write down the answers to these.

1. 18 – 5   2. 12 + 0   3. 20 – 7
4. 15 – 9   5. 7 + 8   6. 17 – 9
7. 15 + 4   8. 11 + 9

◀◀
Exercises 4
and 5 on
pages 16
and 17

B 1.   96   2.   59   3.   73   4.   64
             – 33   +26   – 59   +28

◀◀
Exercise 6
on page 17

C 1. Ming's 3 darts hit the board
         like this.
         How many points did she get?

2. Sally got 23 points.
    Draw a board like the
    one shown.
    Show how Sally's 3 darts
    hit the board.

3. Dan needed 40 points to win a game.
    What is the smallest number of darts he could throw
    to get 40 points or more?

◀◀
Exercises 11
and 12 on
pages 19
and 20

D Copy these and fill in the answers.

1. 531   2. 259   3. 2389   4. 3432
   +265   +321   +3275   +2868

◀◀
Exercises 16
and 17 on
pages 23
and 24

E Copy these and fill in the answers.

1. 287   2. 386   3. 9865   4. 8563
   – 153   – 147   – 6783   – 5778

◀◀
Exercise 19
on page 24

F James and Carol went to France.

1. They spent £153 on hiring a car.
    They spent £469 on hotels.
    How much did they spend altogether?
2. How much change would they get from £800?

TV...

A newspaper did a survey to find out how much TV people watched.

Think of a survey you might do to find out something about TV.

What would your survey find out?

Graphs

Remember . . .

A **pictogram** is a picture graph.

Example   Tina asked her friends what TV shows they liked.

This pictogram shows her results.

Which TV show was the most popular?

TV shows liked	
Home and Away	🖵🖵🖵🖵🖵🖵
Neighbours	🖵🖵🖵🖵🖵
News	🖵🖵🖵
Mr Bean	🖵🖵🖵🖵
🖵 stands for 2 people	

Exercise 1   **A** Green School sold sweatshirts.

This pictogram shows sales in the first 6 months.

Sweatshirts sold in first 6 months	
small	👕👕👕👕
medium	👕👕👕👕👕
large	
extra large	

👕 stands for 10 sweatshirts

Use a copy of this pictogram.

1. How many small sweatshirts were sold?

2. How many medium sweatshirts were sold?

3. 60 large sweatshirts and 45 extra large were sold.
   Show this on your pictogram.

B This pictogram shows sales of sweatshirts in the next 6 months.

Use a copy of this pictogram.

Sweatshirts sold in second 6 months	
small	👕👕
medium	
large	
extra large	

👕 stands for 10 sweatshirts

1. Which of these is the number of small sweatshirts sold?
   20   25   28   22

2. There were 15 medium sweatshirts sold.
   Show this on your pictogram.

3. There were 31 large sweatshirts sold.
   Show this on your pictogram.

4. There were 18 extra large sweatshirts sold.
   Show this on your pictogram.

5. Look at the pictograms in **A** and **B**.
   Which 6 months do you think was the colder?
   How can you tell this from the pictogram?

Remember . . .

This is a **bar chart**.

It shows the number of
sweatshirts sold in the
first 6 months.

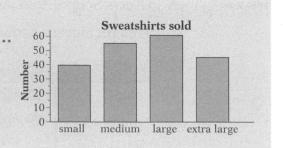

Sweatshirts sold

Exercise 2   **A**   This pictogram shows what
colour pupils liked for
a sports team.

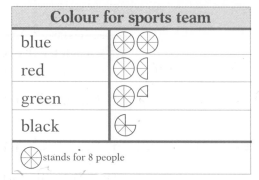

Colour for sports team	
blue	
red	
green	
black	

1.   How many people
does 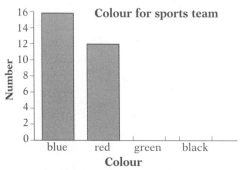 stand for?

2.   How many people
does ◁ stand for?

3.   Use a copy of this bar chart.
Finish the bar chart to show what colour pupils liked.

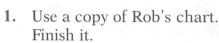

B   Rob wrote down how many glasses
of water he drank each week.

He started to draw this
bar chart.

Rob drank
21 glasses in week 3
13 glasses in week 4.

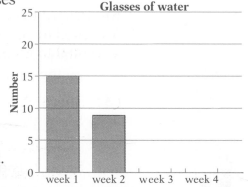

Glasses of water

1.   Use a copy of Rob's chart.
Finish it.
2.   How many glasses did Rob drink in week 2?
3.   It was very hot one week.
Which week do you think this was?

Bar-line graphs

A **bar-line** graph is like a bar chart but the bars are drawn as lines.

Example   Susan asked her friends what fruit they liked best.

This bar-line graph shows her results.

5 liked apples best
3 liked pears best
4 liked oranges best

How many liked bananas best?

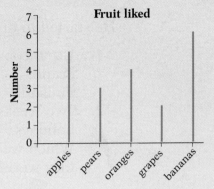

Exercise 3   **A**   Helen asked her friends what meal they liked best.

She drew this bar-line graph.

1.   How many liked roasts best?

2.   How many liked pasta best?

3.   How many liked fish and chips best?

4.   How many friends did Helen ask?

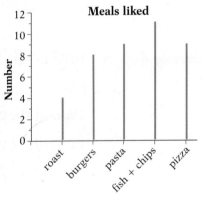

B   Tammy's teacher asked the class where they would like to go for a class trip.

She started to draw this bar-line graph.
3 wanted to go skating.
4 wanted to go swimming.

1.   Use a copy of this bar-line graph. Finish it.

2.   How many wanted to go to the fun park?

3.   Tammy said 'Most people want to go to the fun park.' How can you tell from the graph that Tammy is wrong?

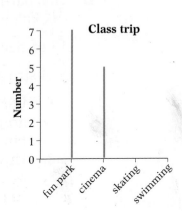

C Tom collected this data about how much money he spent each week.

Week	1	2	3	4	5	6	7	8
Spent	£2	£3	£5	£4	£10	£9	£3	£4

He started to draw this bar-line graph.

1. Use a copy of the bar-line graph.
   Finish it.
2. Two weeks were school holidays.
   Which weeks do you think they were?

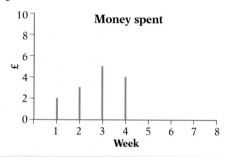

The **number of times** something happens is called the **frequency**.

We often put **frequency** instead of **number** on graphs.

Exercise 4   **A** Julie asked lots of people if they liked school.

She started to draw this bar-line graph.

17 said they like it.

11 said they don't like it.

6 said they hate it.

1. Use a copy of this bar-line graph.
   Finish it.
2. How many said they love it?

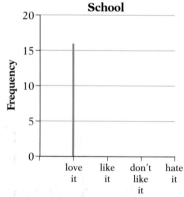

B This bar-line graph shows sales of trackpants at Dale School.

15 of size 12 were sold.

8 of size 14 were sold.

1. Use a copy of this bar-line graph.
   Finish it.
2. How many size 10 were sold?
3. Mr. Lee said '41 pupils bought trackpants'.
   Explain why he might be wrong.

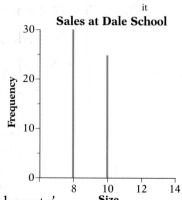

4. This bar-line graph shows sales of trackpants at Brookside School.

One school was a primary school.

One school was a secondary school.

Look at the graphs for Dale School and Brookside School.

Which do you think was the primary school?

How can you tell this from the graphs?

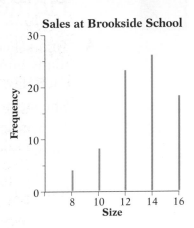

Sales at Brookside School

Task 1

1. Choose one of these.
   school uniform
   shoes
   number of letters in name
   board games
   month born

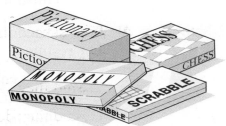

2. Make up a collection sheet to collect data.

3. Collect data by asking people a question about the topic you chose.

Example   Mel chose board games.

He asked the people in his class this question.

'Which of these board games do you like playing most?'

Monopoly   Scrabble   Chess   Pictionary

4. Draw a bar-line graph to show your results.
   Make sure you have
      numbers at equal spaces up the side
      a name for your graph.

5. Draw a bar chart or a pictogram to show the results.

Homework/Review 1

A Tina asked some people how many cups of tea they drank each day.

She started this pictogram.

16 people drank three cups.

18 people drank four cups.

11 people drank more than four cups.

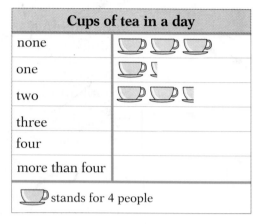

Cups of tea in a day	
none	
one	
two	
three	
four	
more than four	

stands for 4 people

1. Which of these is the number who drank one cup a day?

    4   5   6   7   8   10

2. Use a copy of this pictogram. Finish it.

B Tina started this bar chart to show her results.

1. Use a copy of Tina's bar chart. Finish it.

2. How many people drank no cups of tea each day?

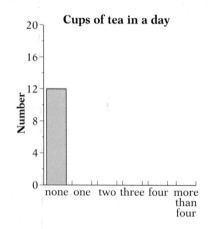

C Clare's class had a quick test of 5 questions.

She started this bar-line graph to show the results.

8 people got 3 right.

13 people got 4 right.

7 people got 5 right.

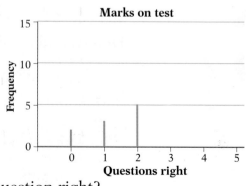

1. Use a copy of this graph. Finish it.

2. How many people got 1 question right?

3. Clare said 'Most people got 4 right'.

    How can you tell from your graph that Clare was wrong?

Collecting data

Example   Liz wrote down what her friends bought at the tuck shop.

Monday	crisps bun baked potato
Tuesday	baked potato crisps crisps
Wednesday	crisps bun baked potato crisps
Thursday	bun bun crisps crisps bun
Friday	crisps crisps bun baked potato crisps

She made this tally chart to show how many of each were bought.

What was bought	Tally	Frequency
crisps	|||| ||||	10
bun	||||		6
baked potato	||||	4

We have used the word **frequency** instead of total.
This table is sometimes called a **frequency table**.

Exercise 5   **A**   Paul sells computers.
Paul wrote down how many children were in each family that he sold a computer to.

month 1	0	3	2	2	1	1	3	2	2	0
month 2	0	0	3	2	0	1	2	2	0	0
month 3	0	2	0	2	1	3	2	0	2	0
month 4	3	0	1	2	0	3	0	2	2	2

Paul started a tally chart to show how many there were of each family size.
Use a copy of Paul's chart.
Finish it.

Number of children	Tally	Frequency
0		
1		
2		
3		

B Enid worked in a book store.

She wrote down what comics she sold each day.

Monday	Beano Twinkle Marvel Beano
Tuesday	Twinkle Twinkle Beano Beano Marvel
Wednesday	Beano Beano Beano Beano Twinkle Marvel
Thursday	Twinkle Marvel Marvel Beano Beano Beano
Friday	Beano Marvel Twinkle Marvel Beano Twinkle

Make a frequency table showing how many of each sort of comic she sold over the whole week.

C Nesta counted how many advertisements there were in each break on TV.

Monday night	5	4	6	7	5	6	4	5	6
Tuesday night	4	5	7	6	6	6	7	6	5
Wednesday night	5	4	7	6	5	4	7	7	6

Use a tallying method to make a table showing how many of each number she counted over the whole 3 nights.

Grouping data

Linda asked her friends how many posters they had on their wall.

These are the answers she got.

7	6	3	2	15	26	32	17	19	26	14	12
8	11	16	21	30	20	19	17	23	24	28	15

Linda made this tally chart for her results.

Number of posters	Tally	Frequency
1–10	IHH	5
11–20	IHH IHH I	11
21–30	IHH II	7
31–40	I	1

Linda put her data into **groups**.
This is called **grouped data**.

Exercise 6   **A**   Penny wrote down how many minutes each of her phone calls was.

8   10   16   3   1   24   25   30   36   17   19   11
16   18   4   3   7   2   1   4   17   19   23   26
28   5   31   17   19   26   11   14   16   25   28   36

Use a copy of this tally chart.
Fill it in.

Number of minutes	Tally	Frequency
1–10		
11–20		
21–30		
31–40		

B   Andy wrote down how many computer games each of his friends had.

4   8   5   7   16   3   11   15   20
14   17   12   13   14   16   7   9   12
14   9   8   3   6   5   12   14   19
8   11   15   19   17   17   16   1   4

Use a copy of this frequency table.
Fill it in.

Number of games	Tally	Frequency
1–5		
6–10		
11–15		
16–20		

C   This list shows the number of days some pupils were away last year.

3   2   1   6   4   21   2   3   5   7
15   12   11   6   5   8   7   2   0   3
0   12   11   13   17   16   5   6   5   8

Use a copy of this. Fill it in.

Number of days away	0–4	5–9	10–14	15–19	20–24
Tally					
Frequency					

Homework/Review 2

A   Ian worked in a shop.
He wrote down what ice-creams people
bought.

Monday	Chocolate Lime Strawberry Chocolate Caramel
Tuesday	Chocolate Strawberry Caramel Caramel Lime
Wednesday	Strawberry Lime Chocolate Lime Caramel Strawberry
Thursday	Chocolate Lime Caramel Caramel
Friday	Lime Chocolate Chocolate Chocolate Strawberry Caramel

Make a frequency table showing how many of each were sold
over the whole week.

B   Dipta wrote down the marks everyone in 7B got in a
science test.

13	16	14	11	7	8	15	9	6	8	19
17	13	19	11	8	3	2	17	18	15	11
10	8	4	7	19	16	14	11	13	13	

Use a copy of this frequency table.
Fill it in.

Mark out of 20	Tally	Frequency
1–5		
6–10		
11–15		
16–20		

Task 2

Choose one of these.

> number of 'e's in each sentence on one page of a book
> number of things in school bags
> goals scored by a netball team in each game

Make up a frequency table which has groups.

Collect your data on this table.

◀◀ CHAPTER REVIEW ◀◀

◀◀

Exercise 1
on page 29

A Kath asked some people which Royal they liked best. She started this pictogram.

15 people like Prince Charles best.

48 people like Prince William best.

32 people like Prince Harry best.

Queen	👑 👑
Princess Anne	👑 👑 👑 👑
Prince Charles	
Prince William	
Prince Harry	

👑 stands for 10 people

1. Use a copy of this pictogram. Fill it in.

2. How many people like Princess Anne best?

◀◀

Exercise 2
on page 30

B Kath drew a bar chart to show her results.

1. Use a copy of Kath's bar chart. Finish it.

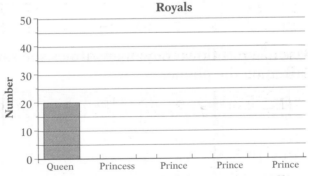

2. Kath said 'Most people like Prince William best'. How can you tell from your graph that Kath is wrong?

◀◀

Exercise 4
on page 32

C Brett started to draw this bar-line graph.

It shows what his friends think of cats.

12 don't like cats.

3 hate cats.

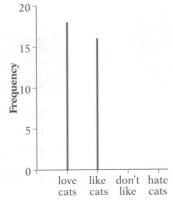

1. Use a copy of this bar-line graph. Finish it.

2. How many said they liked cats?

◄◄
Exercise 5
on page 35

D   Mandy works at a vet's.

One morning she wrote down what animals came in each hour.

9 a.m.–10 a.m.	cat cat dog dog dog rabbit bird cat dog dog
10 a.m.–11 a.m.	dog dog cat bird rabbit hamster dog
11 a.m.–12 p.m.	rabbit hamster dog cat rabbit dog
12 p.m.–1 p.m.	dog cat cat hamster hamster rabbit bird dog dog

Mandy started a frequency table.
It showed how many there were of each animal.
Use a copy of this.
Fill it in.

Animal	Tally	Frequency
cat		
dog		
bird		
rabbit		
hamster		

◄◄
Exercise 6
on page 37

E   Penny wrote down how many times she said 'um' each time she talked on the phone.

3	5	14	8	15	16	5	11	12	19
12	11	8	15	4	17	7	16	13	13
10	13	15	6	7	8	6	7	8	11
20	19	4	14	6	18	8	17	6	4

Use a copy of this.
Fill it in.

Number of times 'Um' said	Tally	Frequency
1–5		
6–10		
11–15		
16–20		

Quick Test 1

Greendale School is having a concert for parents at the town hall.

A Mary's family got these tickets.

Greendale concert	Greendale concert	Greendale concert
TICKET 14 987	TICKET 15 642	TICKET 14 899
Mary's ticket	**Mum's ticket**	**Dad's ticket**

1. Write the number on Mary's ticket in words.
2. What is the thousands digit in Dad's ticket number?
3. Put the ticket numbers in order from smallest to biggest.
4. Mary's sister had ticket number fifteen thousand seven hundred and six.
   Write this using digits.

B 1, Ben sold 123 tickets one week and 89 the next.
   How many tickets did he sell altogether?
2. Sam sold 352 tickets.
   Penny sold 196 tickets.
   How many more did Sam sell than Penny?

C This table shows how many people came to the concert.

	Night 1	**Night 2**
upstairs	1463	1039
downstairs	2676	2568

1. How many came on night 1?
2. How many came on night 2?
3. How many more sat upstairs on night 1 than on night 2?
4. How many more came on night 1 than on night 2?

D Kath asked some friends which Year Group's items they liked best.
She started this pictogram.
15 liked Year 10's items best.
2 liked Year 11's items best.

Year 7's items	
Year 8's items	
Year 9's items	
Year 10's items	
Year 11's items	
	stands for 10 people

1. Use a copy of Kath's pictogram. Finish it.
2. How many liked Year 7's items best?
3. How many liked Year 8's items best?
4. Which of these is the number who liked Year 9's items best?
   15   10   12   18

5. Kath drew a bar chart to show the same results.

Use a copy of Kath's bar chart.
Finish it.

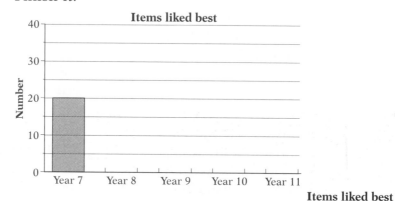

Items liked best

E Bob started to draw this bar-line graph.

It shows which items his friends liked best.

11 liked the band.
17 liked the play.

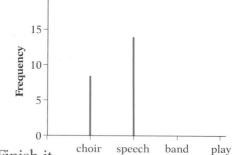

Items liked best

1. Use a copy of Bob's graph. Finish it.
2. How many liked the choir?
3. How many liked the speech?

F Zenta timed all the items in minutes.
These are her results.

3	2	1	2	3	5	4
5	1	3	6	8	16	12
9	4	12	6	3	14	11

Use a copy of this.
Fill it in.

Number of minutes	Tally	Frequency
1–4		
5–8		
9–12		
13–16		

4 Symmetry

Road Signs..

These road signs are used all over the world.

What do they mean?

Which ones are symmetrical?

Lines of symmetry

Remember . . .

The dashed lines are
lines of symmetry.

They are sometimes
called **mirror lines**.

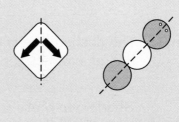

Some shapes have more
than one line of symmetry.

This shape has **4** lines
of symmetry.

Exercise 1   Use a copy of this.

Draw on all the lines of symmetry.

1.    2. 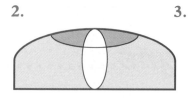   3.

4.    5.    6.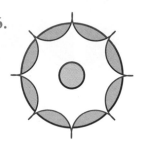

7. 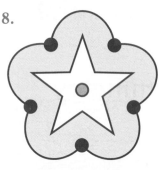   8.

Example   The dashed line is to be a
line of symmetry.

Shade one more square
to make the shape symmetrical.

Answer   We can use a mirror or tracing
paper to see which square to shade.

This shape is now symmetrical.

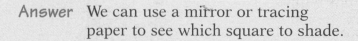
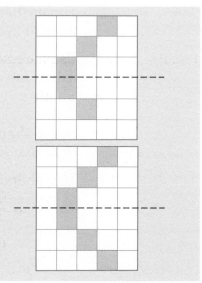

Exercise 2   Use a copy of this.

Shade one more square to make the dashed line a mirror line.

1.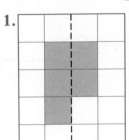

2.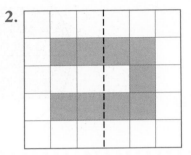

3.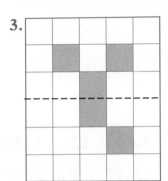

4.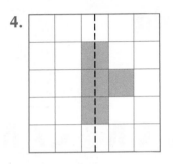

5.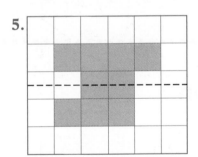

Exercise 3   Use a copy of this.

A Shade **6 more** dots so that the dashed line is a line of symmetry.

1.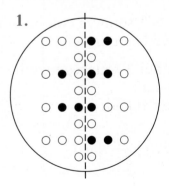

2.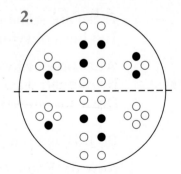

B   Shade **9 more** dots so that *both* dashed lines are lines of symmetry.

1.

2.

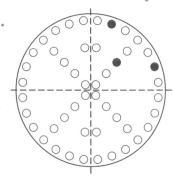

Puzzle

This message has been written using symmetrical letters.

Use a copy of this.
Finish each letter so that it is symmetrical.

ΝLΝ JΛΝ ε ΗοΝ ε 1υϧΛ (
Γο εΛΓ 1ΕΛ ΓΗΛΓ 1 ϹϽϽΚΕͺ

 ## Investigation

You will need   some squares of card

      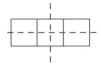

These are some of the ways 3 squares can be put together.
The lines of symmetry have been drawn on.

What other ways can you put 3 squares together?
Draw each way.
Draw the lines of symmetry on each.

Do this again using 4 squares.

Now try 5 squares.

Puzzle

Use a copy of this.
Cut these shapes out.
Put them together to make a symmetrical shape.
There is more than one way for **2** and **3**.

1.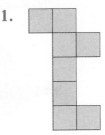

2.

3.

 1 way

 2 ways

 3 ways

Planes of symmetry

This solid shape is symmetrical.

The shaded part is called a **plane of symmetry**.

It cuts the solid exactly in half.

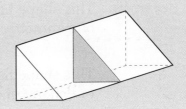

Task 1

You will need Multilink or Lego blocks

Find a friend to work with.
Make a shape from Multilink or Lego blocks.
Do not make it symmetrical.
Swap shapes.
Add some more blocks to make the shape you have been given symmetrical.

Make some more shapes to swap.

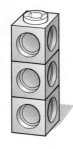

Exercise 4   Which of these solid shapes are symmetrical?

1.

2.
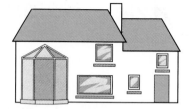

3.

4.
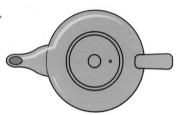

5.

Examples   This shape has one plane of symmetry.

This shape has more than one plane of symmetry.

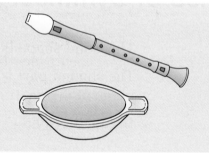

Exercise 5   **A**   Which of these shapes have just one plane of symmetry?

1.

2.

3.

4.
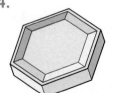

5.

6.

B   Which of the shapes in **A** have more than one plane of symmetry?

Homework/Review 1

A Use a copy of this.
Draw on all the lines of symmetry.

1. 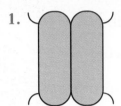   **2.** 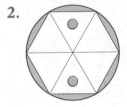   **3.**

B Use a copy of this.

Peter wanted a symmetrical pattern of blue tiles.

Shade **one more** tile to make the dashed line a mirror line.

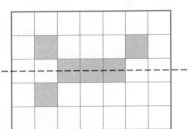

C Use a copy of this.

1. Shade **5 more** dots so that the dashed line is a line of symmetry.

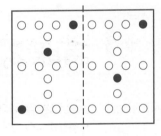

2.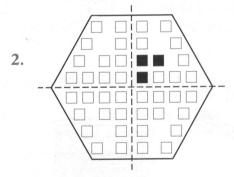

Shade **9 more** squares so that *both* the dashed lines are lines of symmetry.

D Which of these shapes has just one plane of symmetry?

1.    **2.** 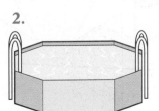   **3.**

E Which of the shapes in **D** has more than one plane of symmetry?

Rotational symmetry

Gary traced this shape.

He turned it a full turn.
It looked the same in three
different positions as he turned it.

This shape has rotational symmetry.

Brenda traced this shape.

Brenda turned this shape a full turn.
It looked the same in only one position
as she turned it.

This shape has **not** got rotational
symmetry.

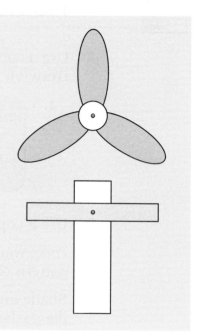

Task 2

You will need   tracing paper
a pin

Trace each of the shapes below.
Put the tracing exactly on top of the shape.
Put a pin through the dot.
Turn the traced shape one whole turn.
How many times does the tracing fit exactly over the shape?

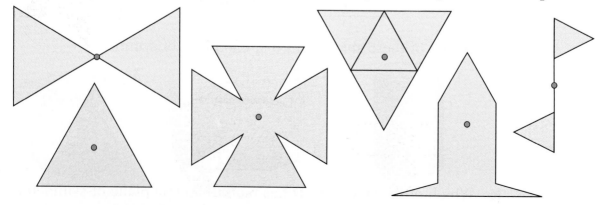

Exercise 6   Do these shapes have rotational symmetry?

Write **yes** or **no**.

You may use tracing paper if you wish.

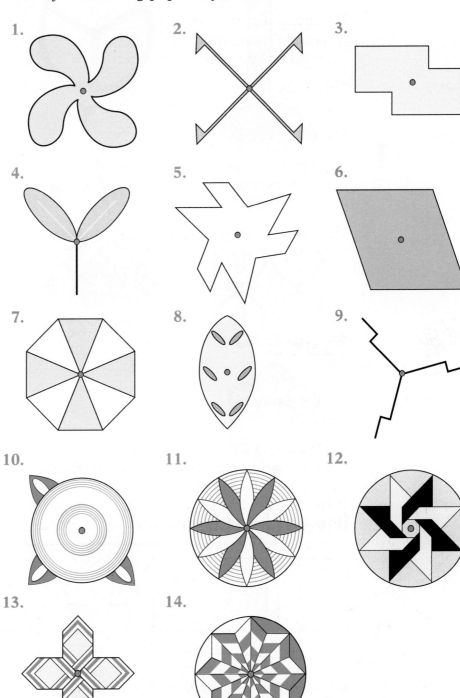

Exercise 7

These shapes are turned through one whole turn.
How many times will they look the same?

Investigation

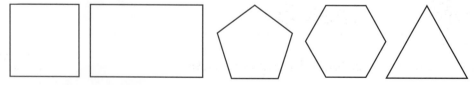

Trace these shapes.
Draw on all the lines of symmetry.
Which ones have rotational symmetry?
Write down the number of times they look the same in a
whole turn.

Homework/Review 2

A Do these shapes have rotational symmetry?
Write **yes** or **no**.
You may use tracing paper if you wish.

1.

2.

3.

4.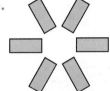

5.

B How many times will these shapes look the same in one whole turn?

1.

2.

3.

4.

5.

6.

Task 3

You will **need**   coloured pencils or pens

Use a copy of this.

Colour this shape so that it has
rotational symmetry.
Use at least 2 colours.

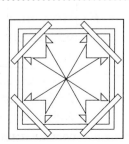

◀◀ CHAPTER REVIEW ◀◀

◀◀ Exercise 1 on page 44

A Use a copy of this.
Draw on all the lines of symmetry.

1. 　　2. 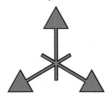　　3.

◀◀ Exercise 3 on page 45

B Use a copy of this.
Shade 9 more dots so that the dashed lines are mirror lines.

1. 　　2.

◀◀ Exercise 4 on page 48

C Are these solid shapes symmetrical?
Write **yes** or **no**.

1. 　　2. 　　3.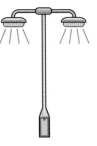

◀◀ Exercise 5 on page 48

D Which of the solids in **C** has just one plane of symmetry?

◀◀ Exercise 6 on page 51

E Do these shapes have rotational symmetry?

1. 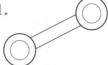　　2. 　　3.

◀◀ Exercise 7 on page 52

F How many times will these shapes look the same in one whole turn?

1. 　　2. 　　3.

5 Multiplying and Dividing

Parties..

Food List – 5 people

3 sausage rolls each

2 small cakes each

10 sweets each

2 packets of biscuits to share

Megan wrote this food list for her party.

There will be 5 people at her party.

- Write down how many sausage rolls, small cakes and sweets she must buy.

- There are 10 biscuits in each packet.
  How many do each get?

- Write a food list for your own party.
  Work out how many of each thing you need to buy.

Multiplying and dividing up to 10 × 10

Remember . . .
....

You should know the **multiplication facts** on this table.

×	0	1	2	3	4	5	6	7	8	9	10
0	0	0	0	0	0	0	0	0	0	0	0
1	0	1	2	3	4	5	6	7	8	9	10
2	0	2	4	6	8	10	12	14	16	18	20
3	0	3	6	9	12	15	18	21	24	27	30
4	0	4	8	12	16	20	24	28	32	36	40
5	0	5	10	15	20	25	30	35	40	45	50
10	0	10	20	30	40	50	60	70	80	90	100

Exercise 1   Write down the answers to these.

1. 6×2	2. 3×5	3. 4×2
4. 2×9	5. 3×0	6. 4×3
7. 5×10	8. 4×6	9. 6×3
10. 5×7	11. 8×2	12. 5×9
13. 4×9	14. 10×6	15. 8×5
16. 3×9	17. 6×5	18. 5×10
19. 4×0	20. 3×7	21. 4×7
22. 4×8	23. 9×5	24. 5×6
25. 10×10	26. 4×4	27. 5×5
28. 8×3	29. 8×4	

Remember . . .

You can use the multiplication facts to work out the answers to **divisions**.

Example $6 \times 3 = 18$ so $18 \div 3 = 6$ and $18 \div 6 = 3$

Exercise 2   Write down the answers to these.

1. $8 \div 2$	2. $16 \div 4$	3. $12 \div 3$
4. $14 \div 7$	5. $20 \div 5$	6. $40 \div 10$
7. $36 \div 9$	8. $24 \div 6$	9. $18 \div 6$
10. $27 \div 3$	11. $50 \div 5$	12. $24 \div 3$
13. $25 \div 5$	14. $28 \div 4$	15. $32 \div 8$
16. $45 \div 9$	17. $32 \div 4$	18. $28 \div 7$
19. $50 \div 10$	20. $100 \div 10$	

Exercise 3   This is a number chain.

Make a copy of it.

Fill in the missing numbers.

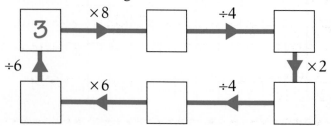

Learn all the **multiplication facts** on this table.

×	0	1	2	3	4	5	6	7	8	9	10
0	0	0	0	0	0	0	0	0	0	0	0
1	0	1	2	3	4	5	6	7	8	9	10
2	0	2	4	6	8	10	12	14	16	18	20
3	0	3	6	9	12	15	18	21	24	27	30
4	0	4	8	12	16	20	24	28	32	36	40
5	0	5	10	15	20	25	30	35	40	45	50
6	0	6	12	18	24	30	36	42	48	54	60
7	0	7	14	21	28	35	42	49	56	63	70
8	0	8	16	24	32	40	48	56	64	72	80
9	0	9	18	27	36	45	54	63	72	81	90
10	0	10	20	30	40	50	60	70	80	90	100

Remember 7×8 is the same as 8×7. 6×4 is the same as 4×6.

The only extra ones that you don't already know are

$6 \times 6 = 36$	$7 \times 7 = 49$	$8 \times 8 = 64$	$9 \times 9 = 81$
$6 \times 7 = 42$	$7 \times 8 = 56$	$8 \times 9 = 72$	
$6 \times 8 = 48$	$7 \times 9 = 63$		
$6 \times 9 = 54$			

Game for 2 players: MEMORY

You will need   20 pieces of card

To play   • Write the 10 new multiplications given above on 10 cards.

• Write the answers on the other 10 cards.

• Turn them all over and mix them up.

• Take turns to turn over 2 cards.

• If the multiplication and its answer are turned over you keep the cards.

• The winner is the person who has the most cards at the end.

Note   You could make cards for any multiplication facts you have trouble remembering.

Exercise 4   **A**   Write down the answers to these.

1. 6×6 2. 8×8 3. 9×9
4. 7×8 5. 8×6 6. 6×9
7. 7×9 8. 9×8 9. 6×7
10. 9×6 11. 9×7 12. 8×9
13. 7×6 14. 8×7 15. 6×8
16. 7×7

B   Use a copy of these multiplication wheels.

Fill in the gaps. $7 \times 7 = 49$ has been filled in.

1.
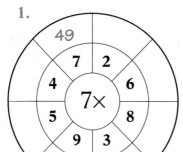
2.
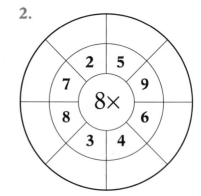

We can work out some more **divisions** from the new multiplication facts.

Examples $7 \times 8 = 56$ so $56 \div 7 = 8$ and $56 \div 8 = 7$

$9 \times 7 = 63$ so $63 \div 9 = 7$ and $63 \div 7 = 9$

Exercise 5   **A**   Write down the answers to these.

1. $49 \div 7$ 2. $56 \div 8$ 3. $63 \div 7$
4. $72 \div 9$ 5. $81 \div 9$ 6. $42 \div 7$
7. $36 \div 6$ 8. $63 \div 9$ 9. $48 \div 8$
10. $54 \div 6$ 11. $64 \div 8$ 12. $72 \div 8$
13. $56 \div 7$ 14. $42 \div 6$ 15. $48 \div 6$
16. $54 \div 9$

B Use a copy of these multiplication wheels.
Use your division facts to fill them in.

1.

| 45 | 63 |
| 7 |
| 81 | 9× | 54 |
| 36 | 72 |

2.

32	48
64	8×	72
56	40

Investigation

What are 5 lots of 1 equal to?
What are 7 lots of 1 equal to?
Write down the answers to these.

| 5 × 1 | 7 × 1 | 10 × 1 | 9 × 1 |
| 20 × 1 | 16 × 1 | 24 × 1 | 18 × 1 |

Copy this sentence.
Finish it.
When a number is multiplied by 1 the answer is _____ .

What is 6 shared by 1 person?
What is 12 shared by 1 person?

Write down the answers to these.

| 8 ÷ 1 | 9 ÷ 1 | 12 ÷ 1 | 16 ÷ 1 |
| 20 ÷ 1 | 18 ÷ 1 | 25 ÷ 1 | 30 ÷ 1 |

Copy this sentence.
Finish it.
When a number is divided by 1 the answer is _____ .

What is 6 shared by 6 people?
What is 8 shared by 8 people?

Write down the answers to these.

| 8 ÷ 8 | 7 ÷ 7 | 9 ÷ 9 | 10 ÷ 10 |
| 15 ÷ 15 | 17 ÷ 17 | 25 ÷ 25 |

Write a sentence about dividing a number by itself.

Exercise 6

1. ☐ × ☐ = 16

    16 × 1 and 1 × 16 are two ways of filling the boxes.
    Write down 3 other ways.

2. ☐ × ☐ = 20

    Write down 6 ways of filling these boxes.

3. 12 ÷ ☐ = ☐

    Write down 6 ways of filling these boxes.

Exercise 7

pack of 6   pack of 10   pack of 5   pack of 8
cherry cakes   orange cakes   chocolate cakes   banana cakes

1. Sue bought 8 packs of cherry cakes.
    How many cakes did she buy altogether?

2. Mike bought 7 packs of banana cakes.
    How many cakes did he buy altogether?

3. Misa bought 8 packs of chocolate cakes and
    3 packs of orange cakes.
    How many cakes did she buy altogether?

4. Carl bought 9 packs of cherry cakes and
    6 packs of banana cakes.
    How many cakes did he buy altogether?

5. Julie bought exactly 15 cakes.
    They were all the same.
    What sort of cakes did Julie buy?

6. Sam bought exactly 56 cakes.
    They were all the same.
    What sort of cakes did Sam buy?

7. Shana wants 30 cakes for her party.
    She wants them all to be the same.
    Shana could buy 3 packs of orange cakes.
    Write down 2 more ways Shana could buy
    exactly 30 cakes.

Remember . . .

If a number can be **divided by 5** it has a 5 or a 0 on the end.
25 and 50 and 110 and 235 can all be divided by 5.

If a number can be **divided by 10** it has a 0 on the end.
20 and 50 and 80 and 300 and 420 can all be divided by 10.

Exercise 8

A 1. Huw planted 54 bean plants.
He planted 9 in each row.
How many rows did he plant?

2. Ben planted 81 lettuce plants.
He planted 9 in each row.
How many rows did he plant?

B 1. Linda planted more than 80 tomato plants.
She planted 5 in each row.
Linda says 'I think I planted 83 plants'.
Explain why Linda must be wrong.

2. Write down two different numbers of plants that Linda could have planted.

C Anna planted more than 100 cabbage plants.
She planted 10 in each row.

1. Which of these could be the number she planted?

103   110   115   118   120   140

2. How can you tell?

D Dan had 20 corn plants.
He wanted to plant them in equal rows.
He could plant 2 rows of 10 plants.

Draw pictures to show how else he could plant them.

Homework/Review 1

A Write down the answers to these.

1. 5×3	2. $18 \div 6$	3. 4×5
4. 9×4	5. $21 \div 3$	6. $40 \div 8$
7. 3×9	8. 8×4	9. $60 \div 10$
10. 4×3	11. $25 \div 5$	12. 7×5
13. $24 \div 8$	14. 4×6	15. $28 \div 4$
16. $45 \div 9$	17. $32 \div 8$	

B Can you make a fire with one stick?

Use a copy of this box.

T $8 \times 6 = 48$
A $64 \div 8$
F 9×7
S $54 \div 6$
H $42 \div 6$
I 9×8
C 9×9
E 6×6
Y $48 \div 8$
M 7×7

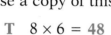

```
___   ___   ___ ,        ___   ___
 6    36     9            72    63

            T
___   ___          ___   ___        ___
72    48            72     9          8

            T
___   ___   ___   ___   ___
49     8    48     81     7
```

C 1. $\boxed{} \times \boxed{} = 18$
Write down 6 ways of filling these boxes.
One way is $\boxed{3} \times \boxed{6} = 18$.

2. $24 \div \boxed{} = \boxed{}$
Write down 8 ways of filling these boxes.
One way is $24 \div \boxed{8} = \boxed{3}$.

D

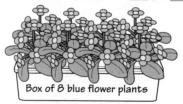

Box of 8 blue flower plants

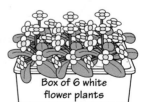

Box of 6 white flower plants

1. Tracy bought 7 boxes of blue flower plants.
   How many did she buy altogether?
2. Ming bought 54 flower plants, all the same colour.
   What colour were they?

Harder multiplying

Sometimes we have to multiply things like 43×2 or 24×3.
We could add.

```
  43          2 4
+ 43          2 4
  86          2ₗ4
              7 2
```

It is often quicker to multiply.

```
  43      43 is 4 tens and 3 ones.
× 2       Multiply the 3 ones by 2 first.
  86      2 × 3 = 6. Write down the 6.
          Then multiply the 4 tens by 2.
          2 × 4 = 8 tens. Write down the 8.
          The answer is 86.
```

Exercise 9   Use a copy of these.
Fill in the answers.

1. 23	2. 44	3. 42	4. 24
× 3	× 2	× 2	× 2

5. 31	6. 34	7. 22
× 3	× 2	× 3

Example

```
  24       Multiply the 4 ones by 3 first.
× ₁3       3 × 4 = 12 ones.
  72       12 is 2 ones and 1 ten.
           Write down the 2.
           Write the 1 ten under the tens.
           Sometimes we say 'we carry the 1'.
           Now multiply the 2 tens by 3.
           3 × 2 = 6 tens.
           6 tens plus the 1 ten carried = 7 tens.
```

Exercise 10   Use a copy of these.
Fill in the answers.

1. 24	2. 27	3. 28	4. 29
× 4	× 3	× 3	× 4

5. 29	6. 19	7. 26
× 3	× 5	× 3

Example

$$\begin{array}{r} 57 \\ \times\ 4 \\ \hline 228 \end{array}$$

Multiply the 7 ones by 4 first.
$4 \times 7 = 28$ ones.
Write down the 8 ones.
'Carry' the 2 tens.
Multiply the 5 tens by 4.
$4 \times 5 = 20$ tens.
20 tens plus the 2 tens carried = 22 tens.
The answer is 228.

Exercise 11

Use a copy of these.
Fill in the answers.

1. 54 $\times\ 3$	2. 27 $\times\ 5$	3. 46 $\times\ 3$	4. 82 $\times\ 3$
5. 38 $\times\ 4$	6. 56 $\times\ 5$	7. 27 $\times\ 6$	8. 34 $\times\ 7$
9. 81 $\times\ 3$	10. 52 $\times\ 5$	11. 60 $\times\ 6$	12. 73 $\times\ 5$
13. 64 $\times\ 5$	14. 45 $\times\ 6$	15. 73 $\times\ 7$	16. 29 $\times\ 4$
17. 19 $\times\ 8$	18. 67 $\times\ 6$	19. 58 $\times\ 4$	20. 36 $\times\ 9$
21. 44 $\times\ 4$	22. 37 $\times\ 8$	23. 23 $\times\ 9$	

Exercise 12

Use a copy of these.
Fill them in.

1.

×	27	35	43
5			
7			
4			

2.

×	25	37	18
6			
9			
8			

Example   Carl bought 5 Beano comics.

How much did this cost altogether?

Answer   We must multiply 45 by 5.

$$\begin{array}{r} 45 \\ \times\,_2 5 \\ \hline 225 \end{array}$$ They cost 225 pence. This is £2.25.

Exercise 13   **A**

1. Gareth bought 6 packets of M&Ms.
   How much did this cost altogether?

2. Chris bought 5 Aero bars.
   How much did this cost altogether?

3. David bought 7 packets of Munchies.
   How much did this cost altogether?

4. Lisa bought 8 Twix bars.
   How much did this cost altogether?

B

1. Jill bought the letters J, I, L, L.
   How much did this cost altogether?

2. Sue bought the letters of her name.
   How much did this cost altogether?

3. Zenta bought the letters of her name.
   How much did this cost altogether?

4. How much would it cost to buy the letters of your name?

Game for a group: MULTIPLYING DICE

You will need   3 dice

pencil and paper

To play
- Take turns to roll the 3 dice.

- Choose 2 of the numbers rolled.
  Make a 2-digit number.
  Multiply this by the 3rd number rolled.

Example   Tom rolled these dice.

He chose 5 and 3 to make 53.

He multiplied 53 by 4.

```
   53
 ×  4
  212
```

- The player who makes the biggest number gets 5 points.
  The player who makes the next biggest number gets 3 points.

- The player with the most points after 10 rounds is the winner.

Puzzle   1 2 3 4 5 6 7 8 9

Choose any of these digits to put in the boxes.
You may only use a digit once in each question.

1.   Fill the boxes to make the biggest answer.

2.   Fill the boxes to make the smallest answer.
   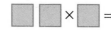

Harder dividing

Remember . . .

Sometimes when we divide there are some left over.

Example   19 apples are shared by 5 people.
They each get 3.
There are 4 left over.

Exercise 14   **A** **1.** Books are packed in boxes of 6.
How many boxes can be packed from 38 books?
How many books are left over?

2. 49 plums are shared by 8 people.
How many do each get?
How many are left over?

B **1.** 29 is divided by 4.
How many are left over?

2. 38 is divided by 9.
How many are left over?

Example   5)39̄   We say 39 ÷ 5 is 7 with 4 left over.
We call the left overs **the remainder**.

We write this as $\begin{array}{r} 7\ r\ 4 \\ 5\overline{)39} \end{array}$

r 4 means remainder of 4.

Exercise 15   Use a copy of this.

Fill in the answers.

1. 7)22̄	**2.** 3)19̄	**3.** 5)27̄	**4.** 6)29̄
5. 8)35̄	**6.** 7)30̄	**7.** 4)36̄	**8.** 6)43̄
9. 3)28̄	**10.** 8)56̄	**11.** 9)47̄	**12.** 7)63̄
13. 8)66̄	**14.** 9)75̄	**15.** 5)47̄	**16.** 8)51̄
17. 7)52̄	**18.** 6)49̄		

Example   68 sweets are shared by 2 people.
How many does each get?

Answer   We must divide 68 by 2.
We write this as   2)68‾

$$\begin{array}{r} 34 \\ \overline{2)68} \end{array}$$

We divide the 6 tens by 2 first.
$6 \div 2 = 3$. Write 3 above the 6.
Now we divide the 8 ones by 2.
$8 \div 2 = 4$. Write 4 above the 8.

They get 34 sweets each.

Exercise 16   Use a copy of these.

Fill in the answers.

1. 4)84   2. 3)36   3. 5)55   4. 2)86

5. 3)63   6. 4)48   7. 2)64   8. 8)88

9. 4)88   10. 3)93   11. 4)84   12. 2)68

13. 2)46   14. 3)99   15. 2)66

Example   78 chocolate bars are shared by 3 families.
How many does each family get?

Answer   We must divide 78 by 3.

$$\begin{array}{r} 2\,6 \\ \overline{3)7\,{}^18} \end{array}$$

We divide the 7 tens by 3 first.
$7 \div 3 = 2$ tens and 1 ten left over.
We write the 2 above the 7.
We make the ten left over into 10 ones.
We now have 18 ones.
Now divide the 18 ones by 3.
$18 \div 3 = 6$.
We write the 6 above the 8.

If we had 80 chocolate bars instead, we divide like this.

$$\begin{array}{r} 2\,6\ r\ 2 \\ \overline{3)8\,{}^20} \end{array}$$

$8 \div 3 = 2$ with 2 tens left over.
The 2 tens become 20 ones.
We now have 20 ones.
$20 \div 3 = 6$ with 2 ones left over.

Exercise 17

Use a copy of these.

Fill in the answers.

1. $4\overline{)60}$ 2. $5\overline{)75}$ 3. $6\overline{)84}$ 4. $3\overline{)81}$

5. $7\overline{)84}$ 6. $4\overline{)64}$ 7. $3\overline{)89}$ 8. $6\overline{)94}$

9. $5\overline{)83}$ 10. $6\overline{)82}$ 11. $4\overline{)57}$ 12. $5\overline{)69}$

13. $4\overline{)75}$ 14. $7\overline{)86}$ 15. $6\overline{)93}$ 16. $4\overline{)53}$

17. $7\overline{)95}$ 18. $2\overline{)63}$ 19. $8\overline{)92}$ 20. $3\overline{)56}$

21. $6\overline{)73}$ 22. $5\overline{)93}$ 23. $6\overline{)89}$ 24. $4\overline{)87}$

Exercise 18

Fizz Balls **5p**   Snow Drops **7p**   Green Dogs **8p**   Black Cats **4p**

A 1. How many Fizz Balls could Jon buy with 95 p?

2. How many Snow Drops could Gill buy with 98 p?

3. How many Green Dogs could Pat buy with 96 p?

4. How many Black Cats could Selma buy with 92 p?

B 1. Pinder had 88 p in her pocket.
How many Snow Drops could she buy?
How much would she have left?

2. Jo had 93 p in her pocket.
How many Fizz Balls could she buy?
How much would she have left?

3. Jake had 99 p in his pocket.
How many Black Cats could he buy?
How much would he have left?

C Steve had 96 p in his pocket.
He bought 8 Snow Drops.
How many Black Cats could he buy with the change?

Homework/Review 2

A   Use a copy of this.
Fill in the answers.

    1. 23   2. 31   3. 56   4. 68
       × 2   × 3   × 4   × 5

    5. 63   6. 82   7. 73
       × 7   × 6   × 9

B

£23

£89

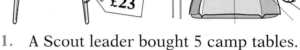

£47

1.   A Scout leader bought 5 camp tables.
     How much did this cost altogether?
2.   A Guide leader bought 6 tents.
     How much did this cost altogether?
3.   A camping ground bought 4 gas cookers.
     How much did this cost altogether?

C   **What happens when you hike across
a river?**

Use a copy of this box.

          7r7
O 8)63
F 5)39
W 3)69
G 7)91
Y 4)84
R 6)83
T 7)97
U 4)87
E 5)92

	O		
21	7r7	21r3	13r5
7r4	18r2	18r2	13r6
13	18r2	13r6	23 18r2 13r6

D   1. Meena makes shirts to sell.
        Each shirt has 6 buttons.
        Meena bought 96 buttons.
        How many shirts would these do?

     2. Later, Meena bought a pack of 88 buttons.
        How many shirts would this do?
        How many buttons would be left over?

◄◄ CHAPTER REVIEW ◄◄

◄◄ Exercises 4 and 5 on page 58

A Use a copy of these multiplication wheels. Fill them in.

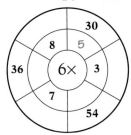 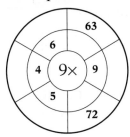 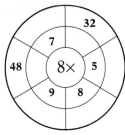

◄◄ Exercise 6 on page 60

B ▢ × ▢ = 12

3 × 4 and 4 × 3 are two ways of filling the boxes.

Write down 4 other ways.

◄◄ Exercises 7 and 8 on pages 60 and 61

C

1. Fred bought 7 packs of basketball cards.
    How many cards did he buy altogether?

2. Thelma bought 56 cards all the same.
    Which sort did she buy?

3. Aled put more than 50 cards
    in his collector's book.
    He put them in rows of 5.
    Write down two different numbers
    of cards he could have put in his book.

4. Sam laid out 18 cards on the table.
    He had the same number in each row.
    Draw pictures to show 5 different ways he could have laid them.

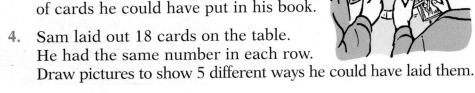

◄◄ Exercise 12 on page 64

D Use a copy of these. Fill them in.

1.

×	54	37	29
6			
8			
7			

2.

×	45	63	76
5			
9			
4			

◄◄

Exercise 13
on page 65

E

1. Mrs. Brown bought 4 fun pencils for her children.
   How much did she pay altogether?

2. Tim bought 6 candles.
   How much did these cost altogether?

3. Laura bought 3 boxes of paints for her sisters.
   How much did these cost altogether?

◄◄

Exercise 15,
16 and 17 on
pages 68
and 69

F Use a copy of this.
Fill in the answers.

1. $\overset{5\,r\,2}{6)\overline{32}}$

2. $7)\overline{43}$

3. $5)\overline{42}$

4. $4)\overline{80}$

5. $7)\overline{77}$

6. $3)\overline{69}$

7. $7)\overline{85}$

8. $3)\overline{64}$

9. $5)\overline{87}$

10. $4)\overline{79}$

11. $7)\overline{96}$

◄◄

Exercise 18
on page 69

G

Pam packs chocolates in boxes of 8.

1. How many boxes will 96 chocolates fill?

2. How many boxes will 87 chocolates fill?
   How many will be left over?

6 Factors, Prime Numbers, Multiples and Squares

Friends..

Ben had 12 sweets.

Could Ben share them equally with 1 other person?

What about 2 others?

What about 3 others?

Write down all the numbers of people Ben could share his sweets equally with.

Factors

 ## Investigation

1.

   Kate tried these ways of setting out 12 pot plants.
   What other ways could she set them out in equal rows?

2. What numbers can 12 be divided by?

3. How many ways could Kate set out 20 pot plants in equal rows?
   Draw pictures to show these.

4. What numbers can 20 be divided by?

   What do you notice about the answers to **1** and **2**?
   What about the answers to **3** and **4**?

6 buns can be shared equally by **6, 1, 3** and **2** people.

We can set out 6 buns in these ways.

**6 rows of
1 bun**

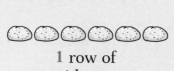

**1 row of
6 buns**

**3 rows of
2 buns**

**2 rows of
3 buns**

6 can be divided by **6, 1, 3** and **2**.
We say that 6, 1, 3 and 2 are the **factors** of 6.

Exercise 1   **A**   What numbers go in the gaps?

The first one is done.

1.   <u>4</u> or <u>5</u> or <u>20</u> or <u>1</u> or <u>10</u> or <u>2</u> people can share 20 cakes equally.

2.   __or__or__or__or__or__people can share 18 cakes equally.

3.   __or__or__or__or__or__people can share 12 cakes equally.

4.   __or__or__or__people can share 14 cakes equally.

5.   __or__or__or__or__people can share 16 cakes equally.

6.   __or__or__or__people can share 15 cakes equally.

B   Use a copy of this.

Cross out the factors of 24.

Cross out the factors of 20.

Cross out the factors of 15.

Cross out the factors of 14.

Which numbers are left?

2	7	3	5
20	6	10	1
24	9	12	15
16	8	14	4

C   Write down all the factors of these numbers.

1. 4	2. 6	3. 8	4. 15
5. 20	6. 25	7. 16	8. 24
9. 18	10. 14	11. 30	

D   Find the number between 20 and 30 which has the most factors.

Example   Find all the factors of 42.

Answer   Use the calculator to help.

We have to find all the numbers that 42 can be divided by.

42 can be divided by 1, 42, 2, 21, 3, 14, 6, 7.

Exercise 2   Use the calculator if you need to.
Find all the factors of these numbers.

1. 36	2. 45	3. 40	4. 44
5. 48	6. 64	7. 72	8. 88
9. 96	10. 68	11. 51	

Game for 2 to 4 players: Factors

You will need   a calculator

10 cards with 0 to 9 written on them
a copy of this board

Name		Factors
_____	☐☐	_____
_____	☐☐	_____
_____	☐☐	_____
_____	☐☐	_____

To play
- On the board, write down the names of all the players.
- Cross out any boxes that don't have names beside them.
- Take turns to take a number card.
- On your turn write the number in one of the boxes on the board.
  You can write it beside your name **or** you can write it beside someone else's name.
- Take turns to do this until all the boxes are full.
- Write down the factors of the number beside your name.
- Use the calculator if you need to.

Example   Jenni Brown [2][8] 1, 28, 2, 14, 4, 7 (6 factors)
- The player with the most factors wins.

Prime numbers

Investigation

Kate set out 5 pot plants in a row.
She wants equal numbers in each row.
How else could she set them out?

What if Kate had 7 pot plants?
What if she had these numbers of pot plants?
    11   13   17   19

How many ways can she set each out?
Write down the factors of each of these numbers.
What do you notice about the factors of these numbers?

A **prime number** can be divided by just 2 numbers.
These are itself and 1.

Example   5 is a prime number.
5 can be divided by 5.
5 can be divided by 1.
5 cannot be divided by any other number.

Some other prime numbers are 2, 3, 7 and 11.
1 is not a prime number.
It can only be divided by *one* number.

Exercise 3   **A**   Are these prime numbers?
Write **yes** or **no**.

1. 3   2. 6   3. 11   4. 2
5. 13   6. 18   7. 4   8. 15
9. 17   10. 20   11. 23

B   Which number is **not** a prime number?
1. 1, 2, 3, 5, 7   2. 2, 3, 5, 7, 8, 11
3. 9, 11, 19, 29, 37   4. 13, 17, 21, 37, 41
5. 2, 5, 11, 18, 31

C   Write down the first 4 prime numbers.

Exercise 4

Start at any number on the bottom row.
Move up one row at a time.
You must only go through prime numbers.
Find as many paths to the top as you can.
One path is shown.

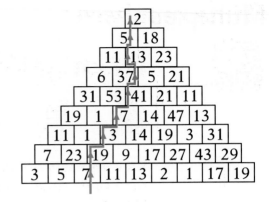

Investigation

13 is a prime number.
If we change the order of the digits we get 31.
31 is also a prime number.
13 and 31 are called **emirp** numbers.
Emirp is prime spelt backwards.
Which of these are emirp numbers?

17   23   29   37

Try and find 3 more emirp numbers.

Investigation

On Mars a special machine makes things bigger.
The 2's machine makes things two times bigger.
The 3's machine makes things three times bigger, and so on.
There are 50 machines altogether.
One day the 8's machine broke down.
Mrs. Mars used the 4's machine and then the 2's machine to make something 8 times bigger.
The 8's machine never got fixed because it wasn't needed.

1	2	3	4	5	6	7	8	9	10	11	12	13	14	15	16	17	18	19	20	21	22	23	24	25
26	27	28	29	30	31	32	33	34	35	36	37	38	39	40	41	42	43	44	45	46	47	48	49	50

The other machines broke down one by one.

Use a copy of the box.
Cross out the ones that did not need to be fixed.
What is special about the numbers left?

Multiples

$4 \times 1 = 4$

$4 \times 2 = 8$

$4 \times 3 = 12$

4, 8 and 12 are **multiples** of 4.

What would the next multiple of 4 be?

Example Write down the first five multiples of 3.

Answer We must multiply 3 by 1, 2, 3, 4 and 5.

$3 \times 1 = 3$, $3 \times 2 = 6$, $3 \times 3 = 9$, $3 \times 4 = 12$, $3 \times 5 = 15$

3, 6, 9, 12 and 15 are the first 5 multiples of 3.

Exercise 5

A Write down the first five multiples of these.

1. 6
2. 8
3. 10
4. 7
5. 4
6. 9
7. 12

B 1. Which of these is not a multiple of 4?

16   20   25   28   32

2. Which of these is not a multiple of 7?

28   35   14   21   37

3. Which of these is not a multiple of 6?

18   36   46   24   30

Exercise 6

1. Use a copy of this.

Shade all the multiples of 4.

Shade all the multiples of 7.

Which letter have you made?

37	24	59	21	27
34	49	54	42	45
13	32	56	14	61
18	36	26	63	47
57	28	38	35	43

2. Use a copy of this.

Shade all the multiples of 5.

Shade all the multiples of 6.

Which letter have you made?

56	54	6	5	19
16	15	13	11	26
46	42	48	28	43
47	24	32	49	51
52	20	36	30	34

Homework/Review 1

A **What do you get if you cross a sheep and a banana?**

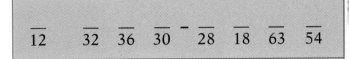

$$\overline{12} \quad \overline{32} \quad \overline{36} \quad \overline{30} \quad \overline{28} \quad \overline{18} \quad \overline{63} \quad \overline{54}$$

Use a copy of this box.
Put an **A** above all the multiples of 6.
Put a **B** above all the multiples of 8.
Put an **N** above all the multiples of 7.

B Find all the factors of these.
   1. 40   **2.** 63   **3.** 56   **4.** 96

C Which number is **not** a prime number?
   1. 1, 3, 11, 13, 19   **2.** 2, 5, 7, 17, 27, 29

D Tom had some tiles.
   He could make a rectangle with 12 of them.

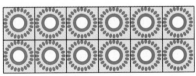

   1. Draw a different rectangle Tom could make with 12 tiles.
   Make the rectangle more than 1 tile long and more than
   1 tile wide.

   2. Tom could only make a row with 7 tiles, not a rectangle.

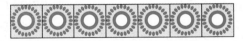

   Write down another number of tiles Tom could **only** make a
   row with.
   It must be bigger than 7.

   3. Could Tom make a rectangle with 18 tiles?

E | 16 | 21 | 24 | 28 | 32 | 36 | 42 | 48 | 54 | 56 |

Write down the numbers from the box that are
   1. multiples of 4   **2.** multiples of 6   **3.** multiples of 8.

Square numbers

Investigation

Ross had some tiles.

He wanted to make a square with them.

He could make squares like this.

1 tile

4 tiles

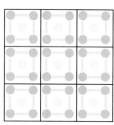

9 tiles

Draw the next 3 sizes of square he could make.

How many tiles are in each?

Copy this sentence and fill in the gaps.

The first 6 numbers of tiles that we can make squares with are 1 , — , — , — , — *and* — .

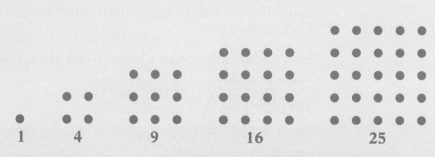

1   4   9   16   25

1, 4, 9, 16 and 25 are examples of square numbers

When we multiply a number by itself the answer is a square number.

Examples $4 \times 4 = 16$ $7 \times 7 = 49$

16 and 49 are square numbers.

Exercise 7   **A**   Are these square numbers?
Write **yes** or **no**.

You can use dot pictures to help if you want to.

1. 25   2. 36   3. 20   4. 48
5. 81   6. 64   7. 100

B   Use a copy of this.

Shade all the square numbers.

Write them all down.

×	1	2	3	4	5	6	7	8	9	10
1	1	2	3	4	5	6	7	8	9	10
2	2	4	6	8	10	12	14	16	18	20
3	3	6	9	12	15	18	21	24	27	30
4	4	8	12	16	20	24	28	32	36	40
5	5	10	15	20	25	30	35	40	45	50
6	6	12	18	24	30	36	42	48	54	60
7	7	14	21	28	35	42	49	56	63	70
8	8	16	24	32	40	48	56	64	72	80
9	9	18	27	36	45	54	63	72	81	90
10	10	20	30	40	50	60	70	80	90	100

Prime numbers, multiples, factors and squares

Exercise 8   **A** | 2   4   8   9   10   16   19   24   29   36   42   49 |

Write down the numbers from the box that are

1. multiples of 4
2. factors of 20
3. prime numbers
4. factors of 24
5. multiples of 6
6. square numbers.

B   Write down the numbers from the ring that are

1. factors of 48
2. multiples of 3
3. square numbers
4. prime numbers.

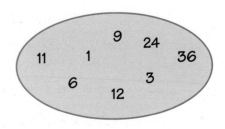

C Use a copy of this diagram.

Shade the parts with

1. factors of 15

2. square numbers

3. multiples of 7

4. prime numbers.

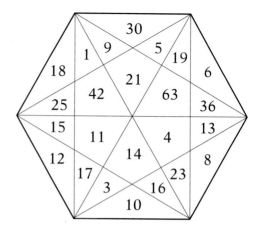

D

| prime   factors   square   multiples |

Which of the words in the box goes in the gap?

1. 2, 7, 11, 13, 23 are all ———— numbers.

2. 1, 2, 4, 8 are all ———— of 16.

3. 7, 14, 21, 28, 35 are all ———— of 7.

4. 1, 4, 9, 16, 25, 36 are all ———— numbers.

Puzzle   What number am I?

1. I am an even number.

I am less than 15.

I am bigger than 10.

I am a multiple of 3.

What number am I?

2. I am a multiple of 6.

I am also a multiple of 4.

I am less than 15.

What number am I?

3. I am a prime number.

I am a factor of 20.

I am not a factor of 8.

What number am I?

4. I am a square number.

I am a factor of 24.

I am bigger than 2.

What number am I?

Homework/Review 2

A Brad wants to make a square with tiles. Can he make a square with these numbers of tiles?

1. 16   2. 20   3. 25   4. 30

B Use a copy of this.
Shade all the square numbers.

72	58	1	3	2
26	96	16	7	8
81	36	4	25	9
24	32	49	38	21
70	61	64	40	17

C Use a copy of this.

A	16	7	21	D	C	B	7	2	11	16	12	6	E
2	40	28	8	9	1	8	24	21	13	29	23	12	8
51	11	23	4	36	27	45	3	5	25	24	19	20	1
33	17	19	25	20	17	63	6	12	2	18	17	10	18
16	31	29	49	32	83	54	22	18	4	30	5	40	4
F	G	H	I	J	K	L	M	N	O	P	Q	R	S

You may move ↓ or → or ←

but *not* ↑ or ↘ or ↙ or ↖ or ↗

Which letter at the bottom do you end at? The first one is done for you.

1. Begin at A.
    Move to squares which have **multiples of 4**.
    1 ends at J.

2. Begin at B.
    Move to squares which have **prime numbers**.

3. Begin at C.
    Move to squares which have **square numbers**.

4. Begin at D.
    Move to squares which have **multiples of 9**.

5. Begin at E.
    Move to squares which have **factors of 40**.

6. Begin at C.
    Move to squares which have **factors of 24**.

CHAPTER REVIEW

Exercise 1
on page 74

A Use a copy of this.

Cross out the factors of 12.
Cross out the factors of 20.
Cross out the factors of 18.
Cross out the factors of 21.
Which number is left?

12	3	1	6	18
5	4	8	21	3
10	9	20	2	7

Exercise 3
on page 76

B Which number is **not** a prime number?
   1. 1, 2, 5, 7, 17, 19   2. 5, 11, 13 23, 35, 37

Exercise 3
on page 76

C Write down the first 5 prime numbers.

Investigations
on pages 76
and 80

D 1. Sam had 24 tiles.
He made this rectangle.
Draw 2 other rectangles Sam
could draw with 24 tiles.
The rectangles must be more than 1 tile wide and more than
1 tile long.

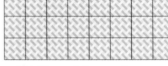

   2. Lisa had 13 tiles.
She cannot make a rectangle with these.
Write down another number of tiles Lisa could not make a
rectangle with.

   3. Joe had 9 tiles.
He can make a square
with these.
Write down two other numbers of tiles Joe could make a
square with.

Exercise 5
on page 78

E Write down the first 5 multiples of these.
   1. 2   2. 4   3. 7   4. 9

Exercise 7
on page 81

F Which of these numbers is **not** a square number?
   1. 1, 2, 4, 9, 16, 81   2. 4, 9, 36, 40, 49, 64

Exercise 8
on page 81

G | 1 | 2 | 4 | 8 | 9 | 11 | 12 | 13 | 16 | 20 | 24 | 31 | 33 | 36 |

Write down the numbers from the box that are
   1. prime numbers   2. factors of 24
   3. multiples of 4   4. square numbers.

Quick Test 2

Greendale School have some new lockers.
Some have a pattern and some have a number on them.

A These are the patterns on 3 of the lockers.
Use a copy of this.
Draw on all the lines of symmetry.

1.    2.    3.

B These are the patterns on 3 other lockers.
Do these shapes have rotational symmetry?

1.   2.   3.

C These solid shapes are in the locker room.
Which have just one plane of symmetry?

1.    2.   3.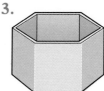

D 1. On one wall there are 9 rows of 8 lockers.
How many is this altogether?

2. On another wall there are 9 rows of 24 lockers.
How many is this altogether?

3. Each locker is 33 cm wide.
How many 3 cm thick books
could fit across each locker?

4. How many 4 cm thick books
could fit across each locker?
How much space is left over?

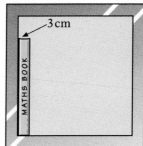

E   8P's teacher made them work out sums to find their
locker number.

1.   Jan's sum was 54 × 6. What was her locker number?
2.   Beth's sum was 3)̄72. What was her locker number?

F   12 lockers were arranged like this
in a rectangle.

Draw pictures to show 2 other ways
they could be arranged to make a rectangle.

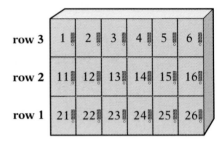

G   The lockers in one corner have
these numbers on them.

1.   Jane's locker is in row 2.
It is a square number.
What number is it?

2.   Brian's locker is in row 1.
It is a multiple of 4.
What number is it?

3.   Wendy's locker is in row 1.
It is a prime number.
What number is it?

4.   Mindu's locker is in row 1.
It is a square number.
What number is it?

5.   Reena's locker is in row 3.
It is not a square number.
It is not a prime number.
What number is it?

6.   Paul's locker is in row 3.
It is a factor of 21.
It is not a square number.
What number is it?

7 Lines and Angles

Building..

Builders often have to check the lines and angles of buildings.

What are the builders in these pictures checking?

What other lines and angles might builders need to check?

Parallel and perpendicular lines

Parallel lines are always the same distance apart.
They never meet.

These lines are parallel.

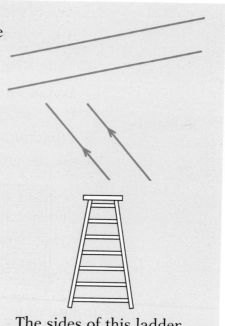

Sometimes we show parallel lines with arrows.

Example

The sides of this ladder are parallel.

The sides of this ladder are *not* parallel.

Exercise 1

Are these lines parallel?
Write yes or no.

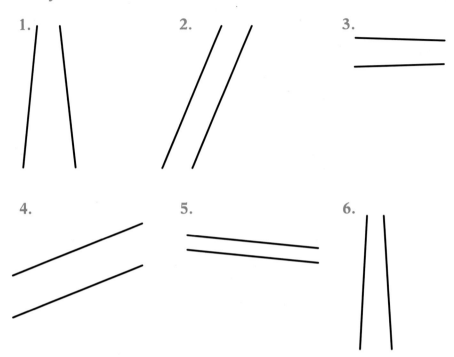

Perpendicular lines have a
right angle between them.

Remember

We use the little box to show a right angle.

Example

The rungs of this ladder
are perpendicular to
the sides.

The rungs of this ladder
are *not* perpendicular
to the sides.

Task 1

You will need   a piece of paper.

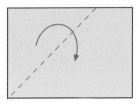

1. Fold the paper as shown.

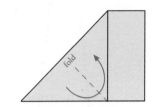

2. Fold it again so the edges are on top of each other.

3. Cut away the untidy edges.
    You are left with a triangle which has a right angle.
    This is sometimes called a **set square**.

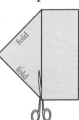

4. Use your set square to see if these lines are perpendicular.

Exercise 2

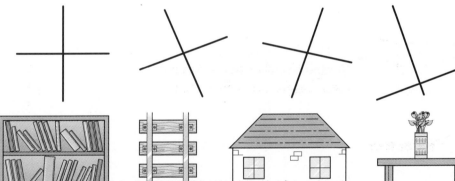

Write parallel or perpendicular for these.

1. the top and bottom of the bookcase
2. the railway lines
3. a shelf and a side of the bookcase
4. the top and the side of a window of the house
5. the legs of the table
6. the side and the top of the door of the house

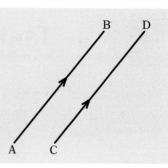

Sometimes we use letters to name lines.
The lines AB and CD are parallel.

Exercise 3

Use a copy of this.
1. Name the lines which are parallel.
2. Name the lines which are perpendicular.

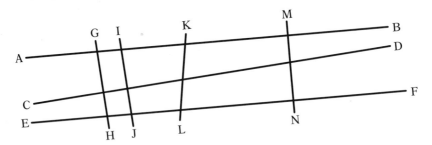

Exercise 4

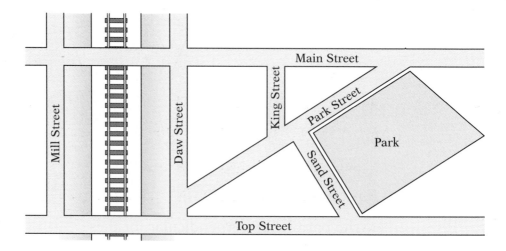

1. Name a street which is parallel to Main Street.
2. Name 3 streets which are parallel to the railway line.
3. Name a street which is perpendicular to Park Street.
4. Name 3 streets which are perpendicular to Main Street.
5. Name the 2 streets which are parallel to the sides of the park.

Task 2

You will need   the set square you made in **Task 1** on **page 89**
a ruler

1. To draw parallel lines follow these steps.

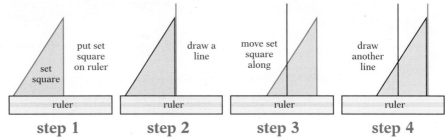

2. Draw some parallel lines.

3. Draw a pattern using parallel
   and perpendicular lines.
   You could use colour in your pattern.

Horizontal and vertical lines

This is a weight on the end of a string.

The string is a **vertical** line.

Vertical lines are perpendicular to the floor.

The top of this wall is **horizontal**.

Horizontal lines are parallel to the floor.

Exercise 5   **A**   Which of these are vertical?

1. sides of a TV set	2. table top
3. kitchen shelves	4. legs of a desk
5. a slide in a playground	6. walls of a room
7. ladder against a wall	

B   Which of the things in **A** are horizontal?

C 1. Write down 3 things in your classroom that are vertical.

2. Write down 3 things that are horizontal.

Angles

Remember . . .

The hands of this clock show a right angle.

We use degrees to measure angles.

The minute hand makes one full turn in a hour.

There are 360 degrees in one full turn.

We write this as 360°.

° means degrees.

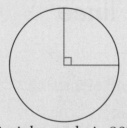

A right angle is 90°.

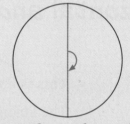

Two right angles make
a **straight** angle.
A straight angle is 180°.

Exercise 6   **A** | 90°   180°   360° |

What goes in the gap?
Choose from the box.

1. A right angle is _____ .   **2.** A full turn is _____ .

3. A half turn is _____ .   **4.** 4 right angles are _____ .

5. 2 right angles are _____ .   **6.** A quarter turn is _____ .

B 1. Which of these angles are 90°?

2. Which of these angles are 180°?

3. Which are straight angles?

4. Which are less than 90°?

5. Which are more than 90° but less than 180°?

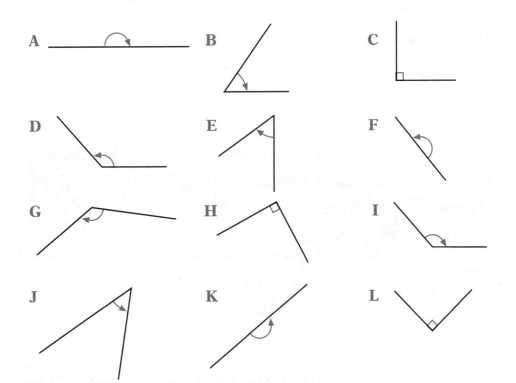

Puzzle

A line has been drawn to the 1 and the 4.

The lines make a 90° angle.

What other numbers could you draw
lines to so the angle between the lines is 90°?

What if the angle was 180° not 90°?

Homework/Review

A   **1.**   Which blue lines in the pictures are parallel?

Write down the letters that are beside them.

Use these letters to make a word.

     2.   Which blue lines in the pictures are perpendicular?

Write down the letters that are beside them.

Use these letters to make a word.

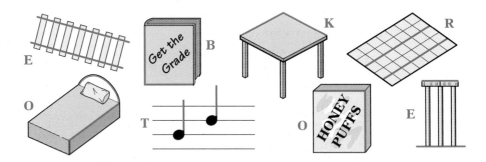

B   Which of these are horizontal?

     1.   the top of a table   **2.**   cricket wickets

     3.   paving stones   **4.**   the legs of a table

     5.   railway lines

C   Which of the things listed in **B** are vertical?

D | 90°   180°   360° |

What goes in the gap?
Choose from the box.

     1.   This angle is ——— .

     2.   This angle is less than ——— .

     3.   This angle is ——— .

     4.   A full turn is ——— .

◀◀ CHAPTER REVIEW ◀◀

Exercise 1
on page 88

A Which line is parallel to the blue line?

1.

2.

3.

4.

Exercise 3
on page 90

B Use a copy of this.
1. Name the lines which are parallel.
2. Name the lines which are perpendicular.
3. Put right angle signs to show perpendicular lines.
4. Put arrows to show parallel lines.

Exercise 5
on page 91

C Which of these are vertical?
1. a wall
2. a floor
3. a flag pole
4. a road up a hill
5. a path

Exercise 5
on page 91

D Which of the things in **C** are horizontal?

Exercise 6
on page 92

E 1. Which of these books is open at 90°?

A   **B**   **C**

2. Which are open at 180°?

Exercise 6
on page 92

F What goes in the gap? | 90°   180°   360° |
Choose from the box.
1. The minute hand of a clock turns —— each hour.
2. The wall and the floor of a room are at —— .
3. A half turn is —— .

Fractions

Sharing...

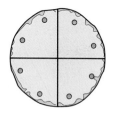 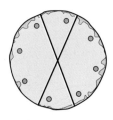 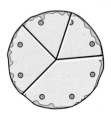 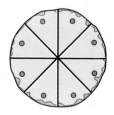

These cakes have been cut into pieces.

Which of these cakes could be shared equally by 4 people?

Which could be shared equally by 2 people?

Draw a square cake.

Draw 2 ways it could be cut so 4 people could share it.

Fractions

$\frac{1}{5}$ is read as one fifth.

$\frac{1}{5}$ means 1 out of every 5.

Examples $\frac{1}{5}$ of these dogs are shaded.

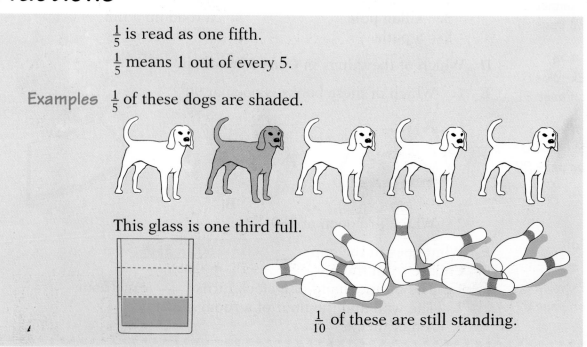

This glass is one third full.

$\frac{1}{10}$ of these are still standing.

Example   What fraction of the whole shape is shaded?

Answer   There are 7 parts.

1 is shaded.

1 out of 7 parts is shaded.

So $\frac{1}{7}$ is shaded.

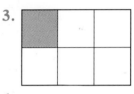

Exercise 1   **A**   What fraction of the whole shape is shaded?

1. 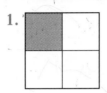   2.   3.

4.   5. 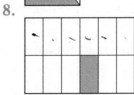   6.

7. 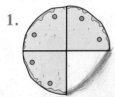   8.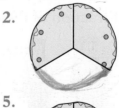

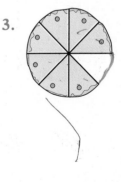

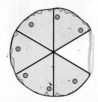

B   What fraction of the cake is missing?

1.   2.   3.

4.   5.

Example   What fraction of the whole shape is shaded?

Answer   2 out of 5 parts are shaded.

So $\frac{2}{5}$ are shaded.

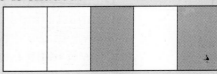

Exercise 2   **A**   What fraction of the whole shape is shaded?

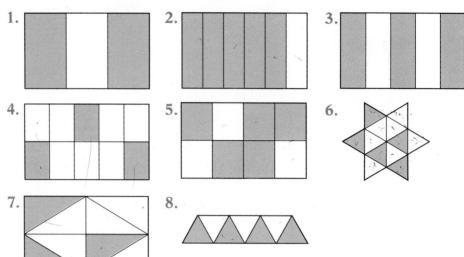

1.   2.   3.

4.   5.   6.

7.   8.

B   1.   What fraction of these animals are dogs?

2.   What fraction of these are blue?

3.   What fraction of these have hats?

Example   Shade $\frac{2}{5}$ of this diagram.

Answer   There are 5 parts.
We must shade 2 out of every 5.
So we shade 2 parts.
Does it matter which 2 we shade?

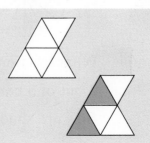

Exercise 3

A Use a copy of this.

1. Shade $\frac{1}{3}$ of this diagram.

2. Shade $\frac{3}{4}$ of this diagram.

3. Shade $\frac{3}{10}$ of this diagram.

4. Shade $\frac{4}{9}$ of this diagram.

5. Shade $\frac{7}{12}$ of this diagram.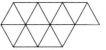

6. Shade $\frac{3}{7}$ of this diagram.

B Use a copy of this.
Shade the fraction that is written beside these.
The first one is done.

1. $\frac{2}{3}$

2. $\frac{5}{7}$

3. $\frac{5}{6}$

4. $\frac{3}{8}$

5. $\frac{5}{12}$

Example   Shade $\frac{3}{8}$ of this diagram.

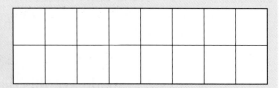

Answer   There are 16 parts.
We must shade 3 out of
every 8.
So we must shade 6 parts.

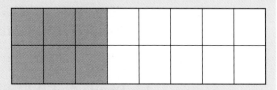

Exercise 4

Use a copy of this.
Shade the fraction that is written beside the diagram.
The first one is done.

1. $\frac{1}{4}$

2. $\frac{1}{5}$

3. $\frac{2}{3}$

4. $\frac{3}{8}$

5. $\frac{4}{9}$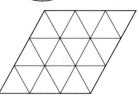

6. $\frac{2}{5}$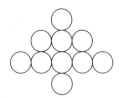

7. $\frac{3}{4}$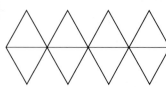

8. $\frac{4}{7}$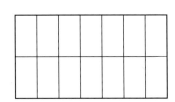

9. $\frac{5}{6}$

Example   Will had 5 chocolate bars.
He ate 2.

1. What fraction did he eat?

2. What fraction did he have left?

Answer   1. He ate 2 out of 5.
So he ate $\frac{2}{5}$.

2. He had 3 left out of 5.
So he had $\frac{3}{5}$ left.

Exercise 5   1. Gary was given 8 tickets to the cinema.
He used 5 of them.
What fraction did he use?

2. Maria had 9 plants.
She planted 7 of them.
What fraction is this?

3. Ross invited 7 friends to his party.
3 of them were girls.
What fraction is this?

4. Gwen bought 4 tops.
3 of them have short sleeves.
What fraction have short sleeves?

5. Milltown has 8 places to eat out.
5 of them sell pizza.
What fraction sell pizza?
What fraction don't sell pizza?

6. The Pet Shop had 6 puppies.
5 of them were sold.
What fraction was sold?
What fraction was left?

7. Rose has 5 cats.
2 of them are black.
What fraction are *not* black?

8. Deri read 10 books last month.
7 of them were from the library.
What fraction were *not* from the library?

Homework/Review 1

A **What would you get if you crossed an insect and a rabbit?**

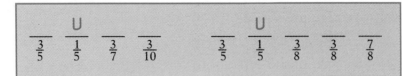

	U					U			
$\frac{3}{5}$	$\frac{1}{5}$	$\frac{3}{7}$	$\frac{3}{10}$		$\frac{3}{5}$	$\frac{1}{5}$	$\frac{3}{8}$	$\frac{3}{8}$	$\frac{7}{8}$

Use a copy of this box.
What fraction of the whole shape is shaded?

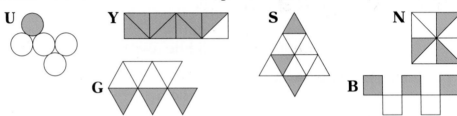

B Use a copy of this.

1. Shade $\frac{3}{4}$ of this diagram.

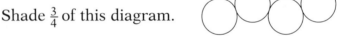

2. Shade $\frac{5}{8}$ of this diagram.

3. Shade $\frac{7}{10}$ of this diagram.

4. Shade $\frac{7}{8}$ of this diagram.

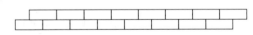

5. Shade $\frac{5}{9}$ of this diagram.

6. Shade $\frac{4}{5}$ of this diagram.

C Tony had 12 minutes homework to do.
He has done 5 minutes of it.
What fraction has he done?
What fraction does he still have to do?

Puzzle

What fraction of these diagrams is shaded?

1.

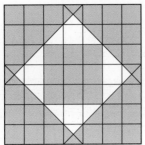

2.

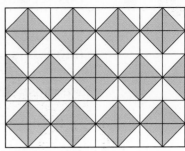

Estimating fractions

We often have to **estimate** fractions.

Example   Julie is about $\frac{3}{4}$ of the way up the cliff.

Task

You will need   some strips of paper about 20 cm long

You need to work in groups for this task.

1. Take a strip of paper each.

2. Cut about $\frac{1}{3}$ off the end.

3. Look to see if you have all cut off the same amount.

4. Do this again but cut off $\frac{2}{5}$ this time.

5. Do this again for these fractions.

$$\frac{3}{5} \qquad \frac{3}{4} \qquad \frac{3}{10} \qquad \frac{1}{8} \qquad \frac{2}{3} \qquad \frac{7}{8}$$

Example Shade **about** $\frac{3}{8}$ of this rectangle.

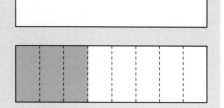

Answer We must first divide the rectangle into 8 bits of about the same size.

We must shade 3 out of 8 of these.

Exercise 6 **A** Use a copy of this.
A fraction is written beside each rectangle.
Shade **about** this much of the rectangle.
The first one is done.

1. $\frac{1}{3}$

2. $\frac{1}{4}$

3. $\frac{3}{4}$

4. $\frac{2}{3}$

5. $\frac{1}{8}$

6. $\frac{7}{10}$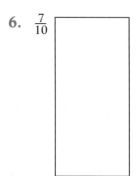

7. $\frac{1}{6}$

B Use a copy of this.
A fraction is written beside each circle.
Shade **about** this much of the circle.
The first one is done.

1. $\frac{5}{6}$

2. $\frac{2}{3}$

3. $\frac{2}{5}$

4. $\frac{5}{8}$

5. $\frac{3}{8}$

6. $\frac{4}{5}$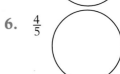

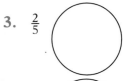

Example   About $\frac{1}{6}$ of these shelves are tapes.

About what fraction are videos?

About what fraction are CDs?

Answer   We cannot tell exactly without measuring.

We make an estimate or good guess.

The videos are about $\frac{3}{6}$.

The CDs are about $\frac{2}{6}$.

Exercise 7   **A**   About $\frac{1}{5}$ of these shelves are cars.

1. About what fraction is trucks?

2. About what fraction is motorbikes?

cars
trucks
motor bikes

B   About $\frac{1}{8}$ of these shelves are small books.

1. About what fraction are big books?

2. About what fraction are magazines?

small books
big books
magazines

C   Tractor A is about $\frac{3}{8}$ of the way from Mill Farm to Oak Farm.

1. About how far along the way from Mill Farm is tractor B?

2. About how far along the way is tractor C?

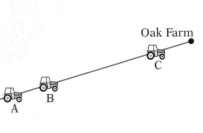

Fraction of

Investigation

What is $\frac{1}{4}$ of 8?
What is $8 \div 4$?

What is $\frac{1}{3}$ of 15?
What is $15 \div 3$?

What is $\frac{1}{8}$ of 16?
What is $16 \div 8$?

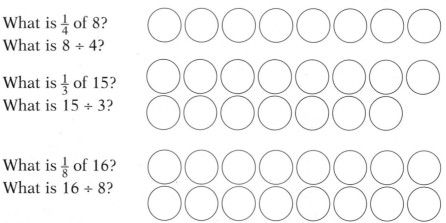

What do you notice about finding a fraction of a number?

Ways to help you find a fraction of

- **By shading**
  If you want to find $\frac{1}{4}$ of 20, draw 20 things.

  Shade 1 out of every 4.

  There are 5 shaded. So $\frac{1}{4}$ of 20 is 5.

  Find these by drawing.
  $\frac{1}{5}$ of 15 $\frac{1}{8}$ of 24 $\frac{1}{3}$ of 18

- **By dividing**
  If you want to find $\frac{1}{4}$ of 20, divide 20 by 4.
  $20 \div 4 = 5$
  So $\frac{1}{4}$ of 20 is 5.

  Find these by dividing.
  $\frac{1}{3}$ of 15 $\frac{1}{6}$ of 24 $\frac{1}{10}$ of 40

Exercise 8

A Find the answers to these.

1. $\frac{1}{4}$ of 4
2. $\frac{1}{2}$ of 20
3. $\frac{1}{3}$ of 21

4. $\frac{1}{5}$ of 20
5. $\frac{1}{6}$ of 12
6. $\frac{1}{8}$ of 24

7. $\frac{1}{4}$ of 28
8. $\frac{1}{3}$ of 24
9. $\frac{1}{9}$ of 27

10. $\frac{1}{8}$ of 32
11. $\frac{1}{6}$ of 18
12. $\frac{1}{4}$ of 32

13. $\frac{1}{3}$ of 30
14. $\frac{1}{10}$ of 50
15. $\frac{1}{5}$ of 25

16. $\frac{1}{7}$ of 28
17. $\frac{1}{5}$ of 35
18. $\frac{1}{8}$ of 40

19. $\frac{1}{5}$ of 45
20. $\frac{1}{9}$ of 54

B Sue has 24 biscuits.
One quarter are eaten.

1. How many are eaten?
2. How many are left?

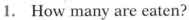

C Ray has a piece of wood, 50 cm long.
He cut one fifth of it off.

1. How much did he cut off?
2. How much is left?

D

TAKE ONE THIRD OFF THE PRICE

Dresses £30   Tops £24   Trousers £27

How much was taken off each of these?

1. Dresses
2. Tops
3. Trousers

E Jan cut one fifth off the length of her friends' hair.
How much did she cut off each?

1. 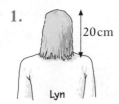 20 cm Lyn
2. 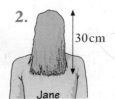 30 cm Jane
3. 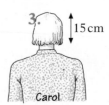 15 cm Carol

Homework/Review 2

A Use a copy of this.

1. Shade about $\frac{1}{3}$ of this.

2. Shade about $\frac{2}{5}$ of this.

3. Shade about $\frac{3}{8}$ of this.

4. Shade about $\frac{3}{4}$ of this.

B Ben is about half way up the hill.
About how far up is

1. Nesta
2. Karen
3. Nia
4. Sam?

C Use a copy of this hill.

1. Meg is climbing this hill.
    She is $\frac{3}{5}$ of the way up.
    Put an M to show where Meg is.
2. Alan is $\frac{1}{3}$ of the way up.
    Put an A to show where Alan is.

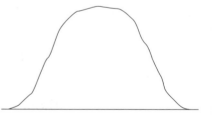

D Find the answers to these.

1. $\frac{1}{3}$ of 12
2. $\frac{1}{4}$ of 20
3. $\frac{1}{5}$ of 30
4. $\frac{1}{6}$ of 36
5. $\frac{1}{7}$ of 21
6. $\frac{1}{8}$ of 48

E Kay had £56.
She spent $\frac{1}{8}$ of this.

1. How much did she spend?
2. How much did she have left?

◀◀ CHAPTER REVIEW ◀◀

◀◀

Exercises 1
and 2 on
pages 97
and 98

A What fraction of the whole shape is shaded?

1.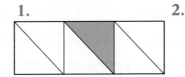

2.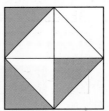

3.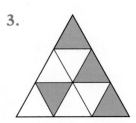

◀◀

Exercises 3
and 4 on
pages 99
and 100

B Use a copy of this.

Shade the fraction that is written beside each.

1. $\frac{2}{3}$

2. $\frac{4}{5}$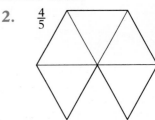

◀◀

Exercise 5
on page 101

C Bright School bought 10 new books.

7 of them were for the library.

1. What fraction was for the library?

2. What fraction was *not* for the library?

◀◀

Exercise 6
on page 104

D Use a copy of this.

1. Shade about $\frac{2}{5}$ of this.

2. Shade about $\frac{5}{8}$ of this.

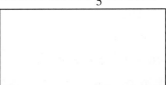

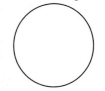

◀◀

Exercise 7
on page 105

E About $\frac{1}{8}$ of this garden is flowers.

1. About what fraction is vegetables?

2. About what fraction is trees?

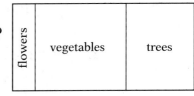

◀◀

Exercise 8
on page 107

F Find the answers to these.

1. $\frac{1}{8}$ of 16

2. $\frac{1}{5}$ of 45

◀◀

Exercise 8
on page 107

G Vijay had a 28 minute phone call to his family.

He talked to his mother for $\frac{1}{7}$ of this time.

How long did he talk to his mother for?

9

Percentages

Facts..

Only 10% of people in the world have enough money to buy a car. 80% have enough for a bike.

33% of English men born in 1953 had been in trouble with the police by 1984.

Almost 75% of the Earth's surface is water.

Think about the facts given above.
What does % mean?
What % facts do you know?
Write them down.

What is a percentage?

per cent means out of 100.
7% means 7 out of 100 or $\frac{7}{100}$.
$\frac{9}{100}$ is 9 out of 100 or 9%.

Exercise 1   Write these as a %.

1. 11 out of 100
2. 23 out of 100
3. 17 out of 100
4. 55 out of 100
5. 47 out of 100
6. 60 out of 100
7. 98 out of 100
8. 86 out of 100
9. 73 out of 100
10. $\frac{5}{100}$
11. $\frac{12}{100}$
12. $\frac{96}{100}$
13. $\frac{8}{100}$
14. $\frac{35}{100}$
15. $\frac{75}{100}$
16. $\frac{87}{100}$
17. $\frac{69}{100}$

Example   There were 100 children at a camp.
53 of them were boys.
What percentage is this?

Answer   53 out of 100 were boys.
So 53% were boys.

Exercise 2   **A**   100 children were asked where they went on holiday.

1.   12 of these went to France.
What percentage is this?

2.   84 stayed in Britain.
What percentage is this?

3.   4 went to Spain.
What percentage is this?

B   Beth's class sat a test.

1.   What percentage did Beth get?

2.   What percentage did Matt get?

3.   What percentage did Jane get?

C   Ramesh's class raised £100.
They decided to spend it
like this.

How the £100
was spent

RSPCA	£25
Save the Children	£60
Land Mines	£15

1.   What percentage went to
the RSPCA?

2.   What percentage went to
Save the Children?

3.   What percentage went to Land Mines?

Example   24 out of 100 squares are shaded.

So 24% are shaded.

Exercise 3   What percentage of these crosswords is shaded?
There are 100 squares in each.

1.

2.

3.

4.

5.

Exercise 4   Use a copy of these flags.
Each flag has 100 parts.
Shade the percentage given beside each diagram.

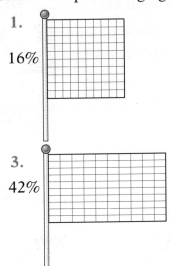

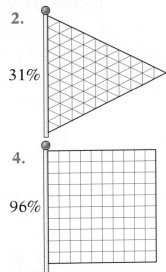

1.
16%

2.
31%

3.
42%

4.
96%

If you got **100%** in a test, you got **all** of it right.
If 100% of a class did their homework it means they **all** did it.
If 60% of a class are boys then 40% must be girls.
60% + 40% = 100%.

Example   70% of a class have blue eyes.
What percentage do not have blue eyes?

Answer   The rest of the class do not have blue eyes.
The whole class makes up 100%.
100% – 70% = 30%.
So 30% do not have blue eyes.

Exercise 5   **A**   1.   50% of a class are boys.
What percentage are girls?

2.   80% of a class know their tables.
What percentage do not?

3.   75% of a class have a pet.
What percentage do not have one?

B 1. Jan and John ate a whole pizza.
Jan ate 45% of it.
What percentage did John eat?

2. John drank 65% of a bottle of lemonade.
What percentage did Jan drink?

3. John drove 48% of the way home.
What percentage of the way home did Jan drive?

C Reena's class did 3 things at camp.

They were asked which they liked best.

climbing	45%
walking	25%
biking	--------

1. What percentage must these add up to?

2. What percentage liked biking best?

D Three people wanted to be class leader.
This table shows how the class voted.

Class Leader	
Jenny	63%
Tom	14%
Sue	--------

1. What percentage must these add up to?

2. What percentage of votes did Sue get?

E A chocolate bar is made from sugar, chocolate, nuts and raisins.
What percentage is nuts?

sugar 33%	chocolate 28%	nuts _____	raisins 15%

F Paul and Lesley went in a skateboard contest.
Points were given for 5 moves.
The total points were out of 100.

1. How many points out of 100 did Paul get altogether?

2. What percentage did Paul get?

3. What percentage did Lesley get?

	Paul	Lesley
move 1	8	5
move 2	16	11
move 3	18	19
move 4	14	17
move 5	12	14

50% is 50 out of 100 which is $\frac{1}{2}$.
So 50% = $\frac{1}{2}$.

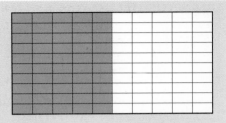

25% is 25 out of 100 which is $\frac{1}{4}$.
So 25% = $\frac{1}{4}$.

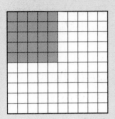

Examples   What percentage of these gardens is planted in flowers?

1 | vegetables | flowers

2 | vegetables | vegetables | vegetables | flowers

Answer   1.   One half is planted in flowers.
$\frac{1}{2}$ = 50%.
So 50% is planted in flowers.

2.   One quarter is planted in flowers.
$\frac{1}{4}$ = 25%.
So 25% is planted in flowers.

Exercise 6   What percentage of these gardens is planted in flowers?

1. | vegetables | flowers

2. | flowers | grass | trees | vegetables

3. | flowers | flowers | trees | trees

4. | flowers | trees | flowers | trees | flowers | trees

5. grass flowers | trees | flowers | trees
grass flowers | trees | grass flowers | trees

10% is 10 out of 100 which is $\frac{1}{10}$.

So 10% = $\frac{1}{10}$

20% = $\frac{2}{10}$

30% = $\frac{3}{10}$ and so on.

Example   What percentage of these have curly hair?

Answer   3 out of 10 or $\frac{3}{10}$ have curly hair.

This is 30%.

Exercise 7   **A**

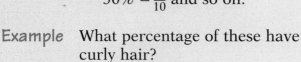

1. What fraction of this scarf is blue?
2. What percentage of this scarf is blue?
3. What fraction of this scarf is white?
4. What percentage of this scarf is white?
5. What fraction of this scarf is black?
6. What percentage of this scarf is black?

B What percentage of these signs is shaded?

1.   2.   3.

Exercise 8   Use a copy of this.

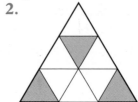

1. Shade $\frac{7}{10}$ of this diagram.
   What percentage have you shaded?

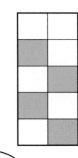

2. Shade $\frac{8}{10}$ of this diagram.
   What percentage have you shaded?

3. Shade $\frac{3}{5}$ of this diagram.
   What percentage have you shaded?

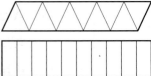

Homework/Review 1

How do you stop fish from smelling?

‾‾‾ ‾‾‾ ‾‾‾ ‾‾‾   ‾‾‾ ‾‾‾ E̶ ‾‾‾ ‾‾‾
60% 50% 25% 77%   40% 60% 63% 15% 23%

‾‾‾ ‾‾‾ ‾‾‾ E̶ ‾‾‾
10% 50% 30% 63% 30%

Use a copy of this box.

E   What is 63 out of 100 as a %?

D   What is $\frac{77}{100}$ as a %?

R   There were 100 children at a concert.
23 were older than fifteen.
What percentage is this?

I   What percentage of this
is shaded?
There are 100 squares.

T   Ron asked his friends which meal
they liked best.
He put the percentages on a table.
What percentage liked dinner best?

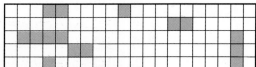

breakfast	42%
lunch	18%
dinner	‑‑‑‑‑‑‑‑

O   What percentage of this garden
is carrots?

L   What percentage of this garden
is peas?

carrots | carrots | peas | grass

H   What percentage of the strip is blue?

N   What percentage of the strip is black?

S   What percentage of the strip is grey?

Estimating percentages

Sometimes we have to **estimate percentages**.

Example   Gill is about half way up
this hill.
She is about 50% of the
way up.
Helen is about $\frac{9}{10}$ of the way
up the hill.
She is about 90% of the way up.
About what percentage of the way up is Ama?

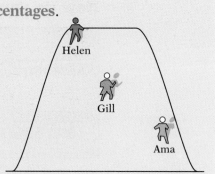

Exercise 9   **A**

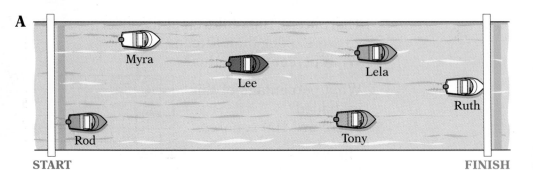

START   FINISH

Some friends raced boats on a canal.
This shows where the boats are after 10 minutes.
The front of Myra's boat is about 25% of the way.
About what percentage of the way are the fronts of these?

1. Lee's boat	**2.** Tony's boat	**3.** Lela's boat
4. Rod's boat	**5.** Ruth's boat	

B

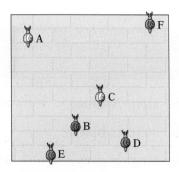

Snails are being raced up a wall.
Snail A is about 90% up the wall.
About what percentage of the way up
are these?

1. Snail B	**2.** Snail C
3. Snail D	**4.** Snail E
5. Snail F	

Example Each class at Mary's school had
to get £100 for charity.

Class 8B had got **about** £60.
They had got about £60 out
of £100.

They had got about 60% of
their money.

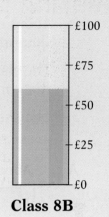

Class 8B

Exercise 10   **A** About what percentage of the £100 had these classes got?

1.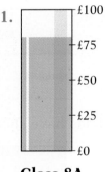

Class 8A

2.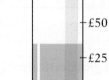

Class 8C

3.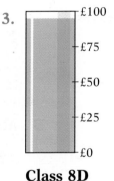

Class 8D

B The percentage of students from each class that helped raise the
money is shown on this graph.

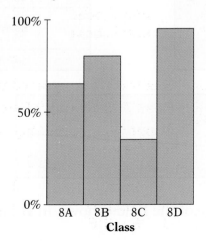

1. About what percentage of
    Class 8A helped?

2. About what percentage of
    Class 8B helped?

3. About what percentage of
    Class 8C helped?

4. About what percentage of
    Class 8D *did not* help?

Example About one half or 50% of a shopping mall is car park.

The shops are a little less than one half of the mall.

The shops are about 40%.

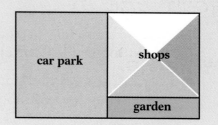

Exercise 11 **A** About what percentage of these shopping malls are shops?

1.
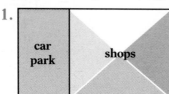

2.
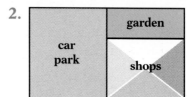

3.
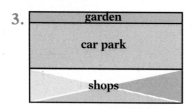

4.
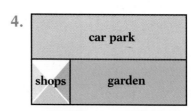

B About what percentage of these fields have sheep in them?

1.
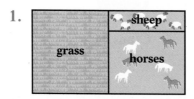

2.
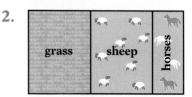

3.
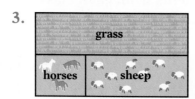

4.
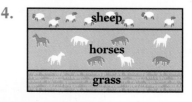

5.
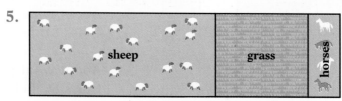

C About what percentage of the fields shown in **B** have horses in them?

Percentage of

Remember . . .

$$50\% = \tfrac{1}{2} \qquad 25\% = \tfrac{1}{4} \qquad 10\% = \tfrac{1}{10}$$

Example   Jon won £20.
He gave 50% to his brother.
How much did he have left?

Answer   Jon gave half to his brother.
Half of £20 is £10.
He had £20 − £10 = £10 left.

Example   Find 25% of 20.

Answer   25% is the same as $\tfrac{1}{4}$.
We need to find $\tfrac{1}{4}$ of 20.
$\tfrac{1}{4}$ of 20 = 5.
So 25% of 20 is 5.

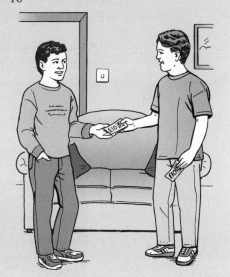

Exercise 12   Find the answers to these.

1. 50% of 4	**2.** 25% of 8	**3.** 50% of 20
4. 25% of 16	**5.** 10% of 20	**6.** 10% of 80
7. 50% of 28	**8.** 25% of 36	**9.** 10% of 100
10. 25% of 24	**11.** 50% of 50	**12.** 10% of 90
13. 10% of 60	**14.** 25% of 28	**15.** 25% of 40
16. 50% of 84	**17.** 25% of 48	

Exercise 13   **A**   Elaine and Chris won these.
They each got 50%.

1.   How much money did Elaine get?
2.   How many bottles of cola did Chris get?

B   There were 40 cats at the RSPCA.
50% of them were tabby.
25% of them were black.
10% of them were ginger.

1.   How many were tabby?
2.   How many were black?
3.   How many were ginger?

Homework/Review 2

A This shows rockets heading to the moon in a computer game.

The front of rocket A is about 10% of the way to the moon.

About what percentage of the way are the fronts of these?

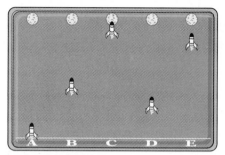

1. rocket B
2. rocket C
3. rocket D
4. rocket E

B About what percentage of these yards are for trucks?

1.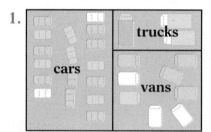

2.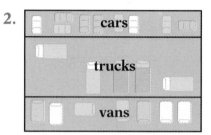

C What is worse than seeing a shark's fin?

$$\frac{}{7} \quad \frac{}{8} \quad \frac{}{8} \quad \frac{I}{6} \quad \frac{}{42} \quad \frac{}{9} \qquad \frac{I}{6} \quad \frac{}{10} \quad \frac{}{7}$$

$$\frac{}{10} \quad \frac{}{8} \quad \frac{}{8} \quad \frac{}{10} \quad \frac{}{5}$$

Use a copy of this box.

I 50% of 12 **G** 25% of 36

H 10% of 50 **N** 50% of 84

S 25% of 28 **T** 10% of 100

E Celie had 32 raffle tickets to sell. She had sold 25% of them. How many is this?

◀◀ CHAPTER REVIEW ◀◀

Exercise 2 on page 111

A What percentage did these get?

1. Vijay
2. Matt
3. Helen
4. Jane

Marks out of 100	
Vijay	85
Matt	69
Helen	57
Jane	89

Exercise 3 on page 112

B What percentage of these have a blue light on?

1.   2.

Exercise 5 on page 113

C 1. 75% of a class are girls.
       What percentage are boys?

2. 10% of a class did not pass a test.
    What percentage passed?

Exercises 6 and 7 on pages 115 and 116

D What percentage of the candles on the cake are blue?

1.   2.

Exercise 9 on page 118

E

Sam   Gina   Nesta   Ann   Maya

GATE   BIKE STAND

Ann is about 85% of the way towards the bike stand.
About what percentage of the way are these?

1. Nesta   2. Sam   3. Maya   4. Gina

Exercise 11 on page 120

F 1. About what percentage of
       this park is playing fields?

2. About what percentage
    is playground?

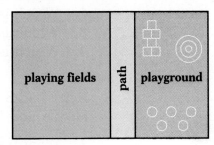

playing fields | path | playground

Exercise 13 on page 121

G Sandy has 8 mice.
       25% of them are white.
       How many white mice has she got?

Quick Test 3

A Keith drew this plan for his new garden.
Use a copy of this.

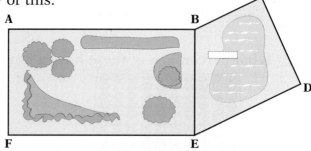

1. Name the lines which are parallel.
2. Name the lines which are perpendicular.
3. Put right angle signs to show perpendicular lines.
4. Put arrows to show parallel lines.

B Which of these are vertical?

    1. fence post   2. garden table top
    3. tree trunk   4. swimming pool cover
    5. ladder against a tree

C Which of the things in **B** are horizontal?

D Some of the angles of Keith's gardens are shown.

1. Which is a 90° angle?
2. Which is a 180° angle?
3. Which is an angle less than 90°?
4. Which is an angle more than 90° but less than 180°?

E Keith had 8 garden beds.
He planted 5 of them in flowers.

    1. What fraction is planted in flowers?
    2. What fraction is not planted in flowers?

F   Keith planted 100 pansies.
27 of them are white.
What percentage are white?

G   Keith is laying some tiles.

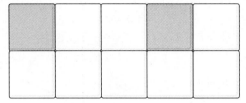

1.   What fraction of the tiles are grey?
2.   What percentage of them are grey?

Use a copy of this.

3.   Shade $\frac{2}{5}$ of the tiles.
4.   What percentage of the tiles have you shaded?

H

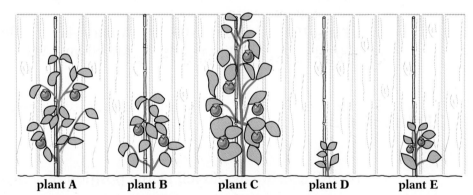

plant A   plant B   plant C   plant D   plant E

Keith planted tomatoes against a fence.
Plant A is about $\frac{3}{4}$ of the way up the fence.
About what fraction of the way up the fence are these?

1.   plant B   2.   plant D   3.   plant E

I   Use the picture in **H** to answer these.
About what percentage of the way up the fence are these?

1.   plant A   2.   plant B   3.   plant C   4.   plant E

10 Coordinates

On the plane.......................................

```
A □  □  □  □  □  □  □  □  □  □
B □  □  □  □  □  □  □  □  □  □

C □  □  □  □  □  □  □  □  □  □
D □  □  □  □  □  □  □  □  □  □
E □  □  □  □  □  □  □  □  □  □

F □  □  □  □  □  □  □  □  □  □
G □  □  □  □  □  □  □  □  □  □
  1  2  3  4  5  6  7  8  9  10
```

Use a copy of this.

Nazir was flying to Greece for a holiday.
His seat number was 8G.
Put an **N** on Nazir's seat in your diagram.
Put a letter to show where these are sitting.

Pat – 7C	Jon – 10F	Anna – 4E	Ben – 6D
Rishi – 1A	Dipta – 5B	Mr. Shan – 9G	

Coordinates

We use **coordinates** to tell us the position of something.

The plane is 4 across and 3 up.

We write this as (4, 3)

across up

The across number is **always** first.

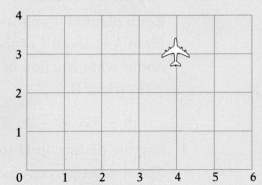

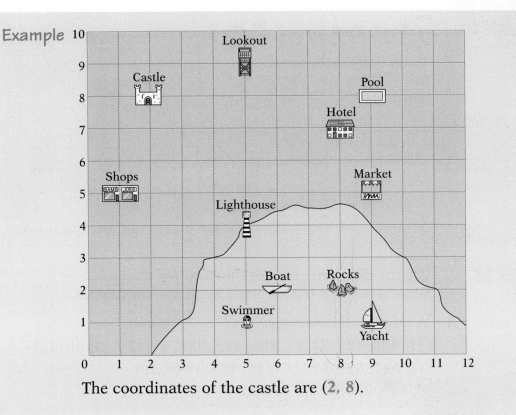

Example

The coordinates of the castle are (**2, 8**).

Exercise 1 Use the map above.

A Write down the coordinates of these.

  1. the boat **2.** the hotel **3.** the yacht

  4. the shops **5.** the pool

B What will you find at these coordinates?

  1. (5, 4) **2.** (5, 9) **3.** (9, 5)

  4. (8, 2) **5.** (5, 1)

C Use a copy of the map above.

  1. Put a hall at (4, 6). Use H for the hall.

  2. Put a tennis court at (11, 8). Use 🎾 for the court.

  3. Put a bridge at (1, 3). Use ⌒ for the bridge.

Example   (1, 4) (7, 8) (3, 6)

The letters at these
coordinates give the
word SHE.

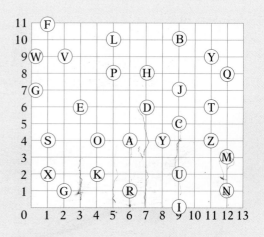

Exercise 2   Use the diagram given in the example above.
Write down the letters given by these coordinates.

A   What does this message say?

(11, 9)(4, 4)(9, 2)   (7, 8)(6, 4)(2, 9)(3, 6)   (2, 1)(4, 4)(11, 6)
(11, 6)(7, 8)(3, 6)(12, 3)   (6, 4)(5, 10)(5, 10)
(6, 1)(9, 0)(0, 7)(7, 8)(11, 6)

B   What are these songs?

1. (9, 5)(6, 4)(12, 1)(7, 6)(5, 10)(3, 6)   (9, 0)(12, 1)   (11, 6)(7, 8)(3, 6)
   (0, 9)(9, 0)(12, 1)(7, 6)   (9, 10)(11, 9)   (3, 6)(5, 10)(11, 6)(4, 4)(12, 1)
   (9, 7)(4, 4)(7, 8)(12, 1)

2. (12, 3)(6, 4)(12, 1)   (9, 0)(12, 1)   (11, 6)(7, 8)(3, 6)
   (12, 3)(9, 0)(6, 1)(6, 1)(4, 4)(6, 1)   (9, 10)(11, 9)
   (12, 3)(9, 0)(9, 5)(7, 8)(6, 4)(3, 6)(5, 10)
   (9, 7)(6, 4)(9, 5)(4, 2)(1, 4)(4, 4)(12, 1)

C   Write down the coordinates for this song title.
   Wannabe by the Spice Girls.

Task

You will need   the diagram given in the example above

Write a message or a song title using coordinates.
Give it to someone else to work out.

This diagram is called a **grid**.

We **plot** points on a grid when we are given the coordinates.

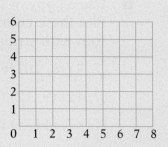

Example To plot the point (7, 3) on the grid we start at (0, 0)

go along 7

go up 3

put a cross or a dot.

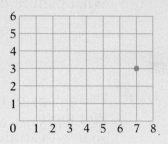

Example This picture has been drawn using the coordinates below. The points are joined with straight lines.

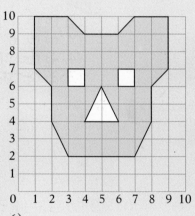

Head   (3, 2) (7, 2) (8, 4) (8, 6)
(9, 7) (9, 10) (7, 10) (6, 9)
(4, 9) (3, 10) (1, 10) (1, 7)
(2, 6) (2, 4) (3, 2)

Eyes   (3, 6) (4, 6) (4, 7) (3, 7) (3, 6)
and (6, 6) (7, 6) (7, 7) (6, 7) (6, 6)

Nose   (5, 6) (4, 4) (6, 4) (5, 6)

Exercise 3 **A** Use a copy of this.
Plot these coordinates.

Join with straight lines.

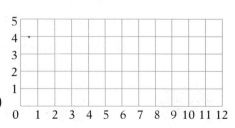

1st letter
(1, 4) (1, 2) (3, 2) (3, 4) (3, 0) (1, 0)

2nd letter
(6, 0) (4, 0) (4, 2) (6, 2) (6, 4) (4, 2) (4, 4) (6, 4)

3rd letter
(9, 4) (7, 4) (7, 2) (9, 2) (9, 0) (7, 0)

What word is made?

B Use a copy of this.
Plot these coordinates.
Join with straight lines.

(2, 4) (6, 10) (6, 11) (5, 13) (7, 11)

(7, 12) (9, 12) (9, 11) (11, 13) (9, 10)

(11, 7) (11, 5) (10, 5) (7, 8) (5, 2)

What picture do you get?

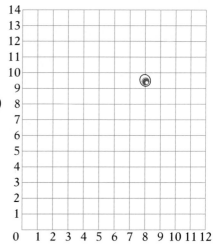

C Use a copy of this.
Plot these.
Join with straight lines.

(5, 0) (5, 2) (3, 2) (3, 6) (4, 7) (10, 7) (10, 3) (9, 2) (7, 2) (7, 0) then
(3, 6) (9, 6) (10, 7) then (9, 6) (9, 2) then (4, 4) (4, 5) (5, 5) (5, 4)
(4, 4) then (7, 4) (7, 5) (8, 5) (8, 4) (7, 4) then (4, 3) (5, 3) (6, 2)
(7, 3) (8, 3)

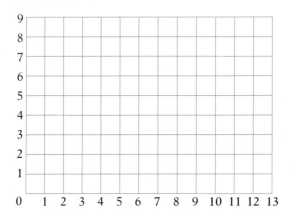

D Write down the
coordinates to plot
this picture.

Begin with (1, 6) (4, 9).

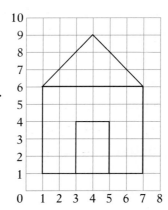

Game for 2 players: GET THE LINE

You will need
a grid like this for each player
a blue and a black dice
2 coloured pens

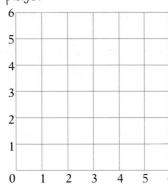

To play
- Take turns to roll both dice.
- The blue dice is your **across** number.
  The black dice is your **up** number.
- Plot the point on your grid.

Example
Ruth rolled these.
She plotted the point (4, 2).

- The winner is the first person to get 3 points plotted in a line.

Sometimes we multiply coordinates by a number.

Both the across and the up number are multiplied.

Example
Multiply these coordinates by 2.

(0, 1) (3, 2) (4, 3)

Answer

$\times 2$

(0, 1) $\longrightarrow$ (0, 2)
(3, 2) $\longrightarrow$ (6, 4)
(4, 3) $\longrightarrow$ (8, 6)

Each number
is multiplied by 2.

Investigation

Use a copy of this.

Karen joined 4 points on a grid to make a rectangle. The coordinates of the points are (1, 1), (1, 3), (4, 3) and (4, 1).

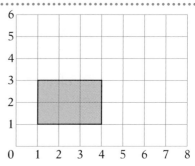

Multiply Karen's coordinates by 2.
(1, 1) ——➤ (2, 2)
(1, 3) ——➤ (,)
(4, 3) ——➤ (,)
(4, 1) ——➤ (,)
Plot the new coordinates on your grid.
What shape do they make?

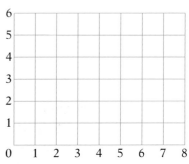

Plot these coordinates to make a triangle.
(0, 0) (2, 2) (4, 0)
Multiply them by 3.
(0, 0) ——➤ (0, 0)
(2, 2) ——➤ (,)
(4, 0) ——➤ (,)
Plot these new coordinates.
What shape do they make?

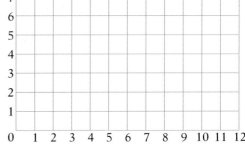

Do we always get the same shape we started with when we multiply coordinates?

Try this shape.
Join these coordinates in order.

(0, 2) (1, 2) (1, 4) (2, 4) (2, 1) (0, 1)

Multiply them by 2.
Plot the new points.

Try some more shapes of your own.

Copy this sentence and finish it.

When we multiply the coordinates of a shape by a number, _____
_____ .

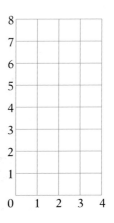

Exercise 4   You will need squared paper
for this exercise.

A Draw a grid like the one shown.
1. Plot these points.
    (0, 1) (4, 3) (4, 1)

2. Join them to make a triangle.

3. Multiply the coordinates by 2.
    (0, 1) ⟶ (0, 2)
    (4, 3) ⟶ (8,)
    (4, 1) ⟶ (,)

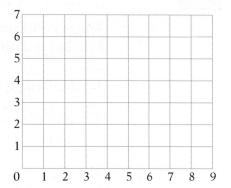

4. Plot the new points.
    Join them to make a triangle.

B Draw a grid like the one shown.
1. Imran plotted these points on
    a grid to make a triangle.
    (1, 0) (2, 1) (3, 0)
    Plot Imran's points.

2. Multiply Imran's coordinates by 3.
    Copy this and fill it in.
    (1, 0) → (,)   (2, 1) → (,)   (3, 0) → (,)

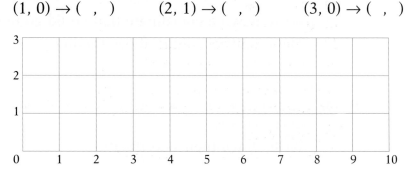

3. Plot these new points.

4. Jackie multiplied Imran's coordinates by a number and
    got these.
    (1, 0) ⟶ (5, 0)
    (2, 1) ⟶ (10, 5)
    (3, 0) ⟶ (15, 0)
    What did Jackie multiply by?

5. Would Jackie's new coordinates make a triangle?

Exercise 5

A Four points on this line have dots.
Their coordinates are
(0, 0), (1, 2), (2, 4) and (3, 6).
The second number in each
bracket is 2 times the first.

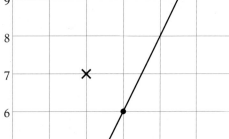

1. Is the point (4, 8) on this line?

2. Will the points (5, 10), (6, 12)
   and (7, 14) be on this line?

3. The point (___ , 30) is on
   the line.
   What is the missing
   coordinate?

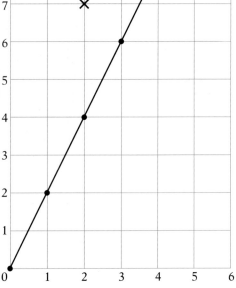

4. The point marked with a
   cross is above the line.
   Its coordinates are (2, 7).
   Which 3 of these points would be above the line?
   (4, 10) (3, 2) (4, 4) (6, 15) (7, 20)
   How can you tell?

5. Write down a coordinate that could go in this gap.
   The point (5, ___) is above the line.

B 1. Four points on this line
   have crosses.
   Write down their coordinates.

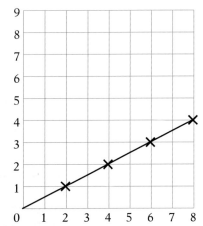

2. What word goes in the gap?
   *For each point, the second
   coordinate is _____ of the
   first coordinate.*

3. Is the point (10, 3) on the line?

4. The point (___ , 6) is on the line.
   What is the missing coordinate?

Homework/Review

A **Why should you never invite a clock to dinner?**

___ ___ ___ ___   ___ ___ ___ ___ ___ ___
(10,5)(5,6) (15,7) (2,2)   (13,3) (2,7) (7,3) (13,3) (2,2) (6,1)

___ ___ ___ ___   ___ ___ ___ ___ ___ ___ ___
(5,6) (13,3) (9,7) (15,7)   (6,1) (15,7)(11,2) (4,3) (4,0) (0,5) (6,1)

Use a copy of this box.

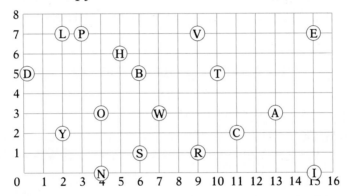

B Write down the coordinates for this song title.
Use the grid above for this question.
Tears in Heaven

C Use a copy of this grid.
Plot these coordinates.
Join with straight lines.
(1, 4) (2, 5) (4, 6) (10, 6) (11, 5)
(13, 7) (14, 7) (13, 5) (13, 4)
(14, 2) (13, 2) (11, 4) (9, 2) (3, 2)
(1, 4) then (5, 6) (8, 7) (10, 7)
(9, 6) then (5, 2) (7, 1) (10, 1) (9, 2)
What picture do you get?

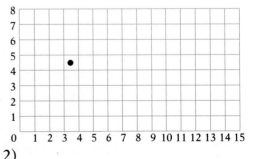

D The coordinates (0, 2), (2, 2), (2, 5) and (0, 5) can be joined to
make a rectangle.
1. Beth multiplied these coordinates by 3.
What are her new coordinates?
2. What shape can Beth make from her new coordinates?

Investigation

The streets of Mathsland make a square grid.

A police officer stands at (3, 3).

He can see a street in each direction.

How many police officers are needed to watch the whole of Mathsland?

Where do they need to stand?

What if Mathsland was 5 streets by 5 streets?

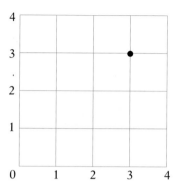

◄◄ CHAPTER REVIEW ◄◄

◄◄
Exercise 1
on page 127

A Jake went to the fun park.

1. He came in through the gate.
   What are the coordinates of the gate?

2. He went to (9, 8).
   What was there?

3. He went to (8, 3).
   What was there?

4. Write down the coordinates of these.
   Fat Lady   Hoopla   Ghost Train   House of Mirrors

◄◄
Exercise 3
on page 129

B Use a copy of this grid.
Plot these coordinates.
Join with straight lines.
(2, 2) (2, 7) (3, 7) (3, 5) (4, 5)
(4, 7) (5, 7) (5, 2) (4, 2) (4, 4)
(3, 4) (3, 2) (2, 2) then
(6, 2) (6, 5) (7, 5) (7, 2) (6, 2)
then (6, 6) (6, 7) (7, 7) (7, 6)
(6, 6)

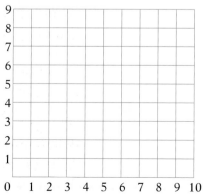

◀◀
Exercise 4
on page 133

C Use a copy of this.

1. Joe plotted these points
    to make a hexagon.
    (0, 2) (1, 3) (2, 3) (3, 2) (2, 1) (1, 1)
    Plot Joe's hexagon.

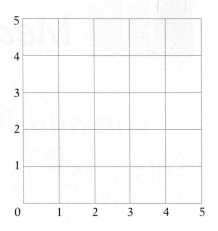

2. Multiply Joe's coordinates by 2.

$$\times 2$$

(0, 2) ⟶ (,)
(1, 3) ⟶ (,)
(2, 3) ⟶ (,)
(3, 2) ⟶ (,)
(2, 1) ⟶ (,)
(1, 1) ⟶ (,)

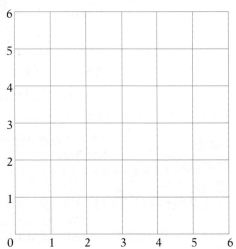

3. Plot the new points on
    this grid.

◀◀
Exercise 5
on page 134

D 1. Four points on the line
        have crosses.

        Write down the coordinates
        of these 4 points.

    2. What do you notice about
        the coordinates?

    3. Will the point (8, 8) be on the line?

    4. The point (___ , $6\frac{1}{2}$) is on the line.
        What number goes in the gap?

    5. The point (2, 6) is above the line.
        Which of these will be above the line?
        (6, 3) (7, 5) (9, 9) (10, 12) (11, 11)

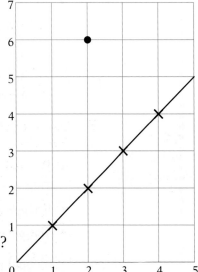

11 Median and Mode

In the middle..

Dipta   Anna   Paul   Anna   Dipta   Paul   Paul   47kg   Anna   45kg   43kg   Dipta

Dipta, Anna and Paul played a game.
They measured their handspans, heights and weights.
The person who got the middle measurement each time got a point.
Who got points for these?

handspan	height	weight

Game for 3 players : IN THE MIDDLE

You will need   a measuring tape
pen and paper

To play   • Write down these eight things about yourself.

1. height in centimetres
2. number of cousins
3. handspan in centimetres
4. length of foot in centimetres
5. number of pens and pencils in pencil case
6. distance around your head in centimetres
7. number in family
8. number of hours you watched TV yesterday

• Decide who is in the middle for each one.
This person gets one point.

• If there is no middle person nobody gets a point.

• The person with the most points wins.

Note   You could play again with 5 people.

Median

Tim got these marks on his last 5 tests.

The middle mark was 7.

We call the middle number the **median**.

Tina wrote down her marks in the last 5 maths tests.

| 3 | 9 | 10 | 8 | 6 |

The marks must be put **in order** to find the median.

    3 6 **8** 9 10

The mark in the middle is 8.
Tina's median mark is 8.

Example   What is the median of these marks?

    3 8 4 2 9 6 5

Answer   The marks in order are

    2 3 4 **5** 6 8 9

The middle mark is 5.
The median is 5.

Exercise 1   **A**   Find the median of these.
They are already in order for you.

1.   2, 4, 5, 7, 9
2.   10, 12, 13, 14, 16
3.   7, 8, 10, 12, 15
4.   6, 9, 12, 14, 18, 19, 20
5.   14, 17, 21, 25, 28, 30, 32
6.   41, 43, 45, 47, 50, 52, 54
7.   1, 1, 3, 5, 8, 9, 9, 10, 11

B   **1.**   What is the median price of these?

2.

£6   £12   £14   £17   £25

What is the median?

C 1. Brenda wrote down the times for some puddings to cook.

apple crumble   35 min   spongy pud   30 min
chocolate pudding   40 min   orange cake   25 min
lemon pie   45 min   caramel pie   20 min
pancakes   15 min

Put the times in order.
What is the median cooking time?

2. These were the times 9 boys took to run along a beach.

25 seconds   26 seconds   24 seconds   21 seconds   20 seconds
27 seconds   23 seconds   28 seconds   22 seconds

Put the times in order.
What is the median time?

3. Jan timed 7 friends to eat a Big Mac.
The times were

$1\frac{1}{2}$ min   2 min   3 min $2\frac{1}{2}$ min   4 min $3\frac{1}{2}$ min   2 min

Put the times in order.
What is the median time?

D 1. What is the median height of these?

Chien   **Brian**   **Jo**   **Vicki**   **James**   **Arvind**   **Lucy**
148 cm   163 cm   161 cm   151 cm   168 cm   153 cm   162 cm

2. Nia measured the distance around the wrists of some friends.

Wrist size
$16\frac{1}{2}$ cm   15 cm   14 cm $17\frac{1}{2}$ cm   16 cm $14\frac{1}{2}$ cm   15 cm   16 cm   16 cm

What is the median wrist size?

Example   Jack got these marks for 6 essays.

10   13   14   16   17   18

There are 2 middle marks.
The median is half way between 14 and 16.
The median is 15.

Example   Elaine got these 8 marks for Science.

21   23   20   25   28   24   27   26

What is the median mark?

Answer   The marks must be in order.

20   21   23   24   25   26   27   28

The median is half way between 24 and 25.
The median is $24\frac{1}{2}$.

Exercise 2   A   Find the median of these marks.
The first three are in order already.

1.   10, 13, 15, 17, 19, 20
2.   7, 8, 9, 11, 12, 15
3.   58, 64, 69, 70, 72, 73, 84, 89
4.   17, 16, 11, 16, 18, 12, 16, 12
5.   38, 36, 42, 51, 69, 73, 42, 25, 27, 38
6.   180, 160, 150, 170, 155, 145, 175, 175

B   Julie put her 8 cats in a show.
She wrote down what mark they got.

Casper	65	Sweetie	65
Nick	82	Hobb	65
Monty	51	Mouser	67
Ginger	79	Major Tom	85

What is the median mark?

C   Gill wrote down the price of a coffee at 10 different cafes.

65 p   70 p   95 p   £1.00   85 p   95 p   £1.30   £1.00   £1.00   80 p

What is the median price?

Sometimes we have to read numbers off a table or chart and then find the median.

Dress sizes sold			
Monday	10	12	
Tuesday	14	18	16
Wednesday	12	12	14
Thursday	10	10	12 16
Friday	12	10	18

Examples

1. What was the median size sold on Monday and Tuesday?

2. What was the median size sold for the week?

Answers

1. We must put the sizes sold on Monday and Tuesday in order.

   10, 12, 14, 16, 18

   The median size is 14.

2. We must put the sizes sold for the week in order.

   10, 10, 10, 10, 12, 12, 12, 12, 12, 14, 14, 16, 16, 18, 18

   The median size is 12.

Exercise 3

A There are 5 teams in a soccer contest.

This table shows the number of goals each team got in their games.

1. What is Team B's median number of goals?

2. What is Team D's median number of goals?

Goals scored in games			
Team A	2	3	5
Team B	6	4	2
Team C	5	6	0
Team D		8	2
Team E	4	3	9

3. Which team got the highest median?

4. What is the median number of goals of all the teams?

B Lyn could catch the Number 26 bus or the Number 18 bus to go home.

She wrote down how long she had to wait each time.

Bus	Waiting time				
Number 26	2 min	4 min	1 min	3 min	6 min
Number 18	0 min	2 min	1 min	7 min	6 min

1. What is the median waiting time for bus Number 26?

2. What is the median waiting time for bus Number 18?

3. What is the median waiting time for both buses?

C Tina asked her friends what their energy level was.

0 = no energy		1 = very low energy	
2 = low energy		3 = some energy	
4 = high energy		5 = very high energy	

She drew this table.

Energy level					
0					
1	Jo	Bob	Nia		
2	Mary	Brenda			
3	Jan	Rob	Sam	Gill	Wyn
4	Karen	Ann	Alex		
5	Peter	Rosemary	Sudi		

She wrote out all the energy levels in order.

1, 1, 1, 2, 2, 3, . . .

1. Copy and finish Tina's list.

2. What is the median energy level?

Homework/Review 1

A **Who does the sea date?**

						E				
72	4½		43	14	4	29		14	74	4½

							E						E
172	72	4½	16		4½	16	4		4½	72	65	4

Use a copy of this box.

Find the median of these.

Only D and T need to be put in order first.

   E   0, 2, 4, 5, 8   U   52, 69, 74, 76, 80
   H   13, 15, 16, 16, 17, 19   S   20, 26, 27, 29, 33, 35, 41
   I   59, 60, 68, 71, 73, 75, 80, 82
   G   40, 41, 42, 42, 43, 43, 45, 47, 48
   W   147, 152, 163, 168, 171, 173, 173, 178, 182, 184
   O   10, 12, 12, 12, 12, 13, 14, 14, 14, 15, 16, 16, 17, 18, 18, 19, 20
   D   26, 83, 51, 79, 82, 64, 66, 48, 86, 83, 41, 37
   T   1, 5, 3, 6, 9, 7, 3, 2, 8, 5, 3, 6, 5, 1, 1, 3, 2, 6, 5, 4

B Jane asked her friends how many videos they had seen in the last month.

She wrote this list.

5, 0, 4, 3, 6, 2, 1, 1, 3, 1, 0, 1, 1, 0, 0, 2

What is the median number of videos watched?

C This table gives the number of people waiting at the checkout at certain times at a supermarket.

Time	9.15 a.m.	10.00 a.m.	10.30 a.m.	11.00 a.m.	11.30 am	12.00 p.m.	12.15 p.m.	12.30 p.m.	1.00 p.m.
People waiting	0	8	12	7	4	15	17	24	9

   1.   What is the median number of people waiting?
   2.   What is the most popular time for people to go shopping?

Mode

Adam sold cars.
He wrote down the number he sold each day for 10 days.

3 2 1 0 1 2 3 4 2 2

He noticed that the number written down most was 2.

We call this the **mode**.

Example   Kelly wrote down how many hours her friends watched TV last night.

3	$\frac{1}{2}$	3	3	1	$1\frac{1}{2}$	2	$\frac{1}{2}$	3
1	3	$1\frac{1}{2}$	2	1	1	$\frac{1}{2}$	3	2

The number she wrote down the most is 3.

The mode is 3.

Exercise 4   **A** What is the mode of these marks?

1. 12, 13, 12, 16, 12, 13, 12

2. 64, 65, 66, 64, 67, 63, 64, 64, 63, 66

3. 8, 7, 6, 5, 8, 9, 7, 5, 8, 7, 8, 9, 8, 6, 5, 8, 5

B These runners got first in races at a school sports day.

What is the mode of their numbers?

Sometimes we read the mode off a table.

Example   This table shows the numbers of each size shoe sold in the last week.

There were more of size 5 sold than any other size.

Size 5 is the mode.

Size	Tally	Frequency
5	ⅡⅡ Ⅲ	8
6	ⅡⅡ Ⅰ	6
7	ⅡⅡ	5
8	Ⅲ	3

Exercise 5

A   Ben worked at McDonalds.

He wrote down how many items people ordered in one hour. He drew this frequency table.

Number of items	Tally	Frequency
2	ⅡⅡ ⅡⅡ Ⅰ	11
3	ⅡⅡ ⅡⅡ ⅡⅡ Ⅰ	16
4	ⅡⅡ ⅡⅡ ⅡⅠ	12
5	ⅡⅡ ⅡⅠ	7

Ben thinks that the mode number of items ordered is 3.

Explain why Ben is right.

B   Karla worked at a clothes shop.

She wrote down how much money people spent.

£	October	November	December	January	Total number of people who spent this amount
£0–£49	5	7	24	5	41
£50–£99	6	8	16	5	35
£100–£149	2	4	12	3	21
£150–£200	3	4	10	2	19

1.   Karla thinks that £0 to £49 is the mode.

Is she right?

Explain your answer.

2.   More people spent money on clothes in December.

Give one reason why this might be.

C Mr Chan wrote down the marks he gave students for homework.

Marks given for homework		
Week 1	**Week 2**	**Week 3**
2 2 1 4	4 5 5 6	4 8 9 9
6 2 3 4	5 6 8 9	7 8 10 9
5 3	4 5	9 9 9 6

1. What is the mode for Week 1?

2. What is the mode for Week 2?

3. What is the mode for Week 3?

4. What is the mode for the whole three Weeks?

5. Give a possible reason why the marks given in Week 3 were higher than those given in Week 1.

D Mr Chan grouped the marks given for homework and started a tally chart.

Marks	Week 1	Week 2	Week 3	Total number
1–3	ЖІ І			6
4–6	ІІІІ	ЖІ ІІІ		
More than 6		ІІ		

1. Use a copy of this tally chart.
    Fill in the columns for Week 3 and Total number.

2. Mr Chan thinks the mode is now 4–6.
    Is he right?
    Explain your answer.

Homework/Review 2

A **Who was the first man in space?**

		E				
___	___	___		___	___	___
80p	50 min	63		60p	40p	£1.60

					E
___	___		___	___	___
£1.20	£1.60		80p	50 min	63

___	___	___	___
60p	60 min	60 min	£1.60

Use a copy of this box.
What is the mode of these?

   E 62, 63, 59, 61, 60, 63, 60, 63

   A 50 p, 40 p, 60 p, 80 p, 40 p, 70 p, 20 p, 60 p, 40 p, 80 p, 40 p

   I £1.20, £1.50, £1.20, £1.60, £1.20, £1.40, £1.70, £1.80, £1.60

   H 60 min, 50 min, 45 min, 50 min, 60 min, 55 min, 50 min,
       48 min, 50 min

   T 80 p, 60 p, 70 p, 40 p, 35 p, 65 p, 80 p, 40 p, 35 p, 80 p, 70 p

   N £1.80, £1.65, £1.60, £1.50, £1.20, £1.60, £1.80, £1.60, £1.20,
       £1.40

   O 60 min, 50 min, 40 min, 45 min, 60 min, 35 min, 50 min,
       60 min, 55 min, 60 min

   M 35 p, 45 p, 50 p, 20 p, 25 p, 30 p, 60 p,
       60 p, 20 p, 45 p, 60 p, 70 p

B Jeff wrote down how many people crossed
the road each time the lights changed.
He did this for 3 hours.

8 a.m. to 9 a.m.	9 a.m. to 10 a.m.	10 a.m. to 11 a.m.
10, 16, 12, 8	8, 4, 3, 0	0, 1, 0, 2
4, 8, 10, 9	2, 1, 3, 2	3, 1, 0, 3
8, 9, 11, 8	4, 1, 3, 2	2, 4, 6, 5
7, 8, 10	5, 0, 2	0, 3, 0

1. What is the mode between 8 a.m. and 9 a.m.?
2. What is the mode between 10 a.m. and 11 a.m.?
3. Later in the morning fewer people used the crossing.
    Give a possible reason for this.

◀◀ CHAPTER REVIEW ◀◀

◀◀ Exercise 1 on page 139

A What is the median price of these?

£6 £7 £8 £10 £12

◀◀ Exercise 2 on page 141

B Terry's friends wrote down what they scored in a video game.
960, 975, 940, 970, 950, 965, 935, 945
What is the median?

◀◀ Exercise 3 on page 142

C Elaine had to go to the doctor each week.
She wrote down how long she had to wait each time.

	Waiting time				
morning	6 min	10 min	8 min	20 min	8 min
afternoon	13 min	16 min	11 min	25 min	15 min

1. What is the median waiting time in the morning?
2. What is the median waiting time in the afternoon?
3. What is the median waiting time for all the visits?

◀◀ Exercise 4 on page 145

D What is the mode of these shirt sizes?
14 10 12 16 12 18 14 12 10 12 10 12
16 14 12 12 10 16 16 14 12 10 12 12

◀◀ Exercise 5 on page 146

E Maya drew this table to show what was spent at a cafe.

Amount of money spent during each hour		
3 p.m. to 4 p.m.	**4 p.m. to 5 p.m.**	**5 p.m. to 6 p.m.**
50 p 40 p 55 p	75 p £1.20 75 p	£1.80 £1.30 £1.70
60 p 40 p 30 p	40 p 40 p 90 p	£1.65 85 p £1.20
55 p 80 p 40 p	75 p 60 p 75 p	£1.95 £1.20 £1.60

1. What is the mode of the amounts of money spent between 4 p.m. and 5 p.m.?
2. What is the mode of the amounts of money spent over the whole time?
3. More money was spent between 5 p.m. and 6 p.m.
Give a reason for this.

12 Decimals

One day...

All of these have decimals.
Today the temperature was 22.5 °C.
Today Tracy spent £16.54.
Today baby Maria weighs 7.6 kg.

Write down 3 more sentences that have decimals.

Tenths and hundredths

This square has been divided
into ten parts.

Each part is one tenth or $\frac{1}{10}$.

We can write $\frac{1}{10}$ as 0.1

$\frac{2}{10}$ as 0.2

$\frac{3}{10}$ as 0.3   and so on.

Example $\frac{7}{10}$ or 0.7 of this square is shaded.

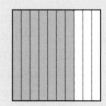

Exercise 1   Write down, as a decimal, how much is shaded.

1. 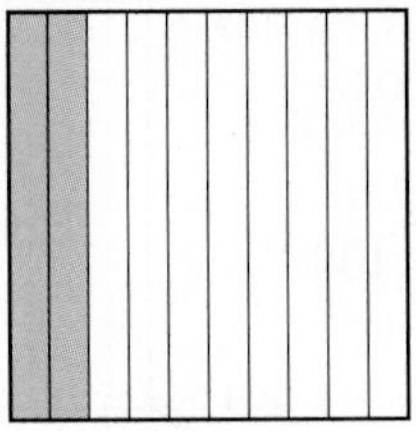   2. 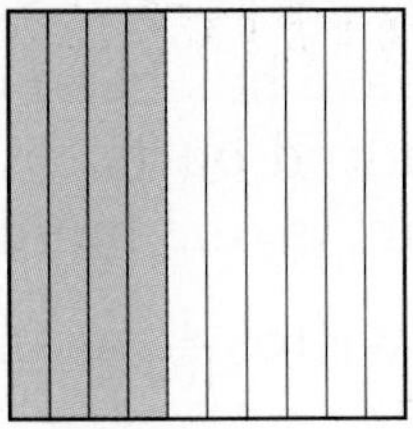   3.

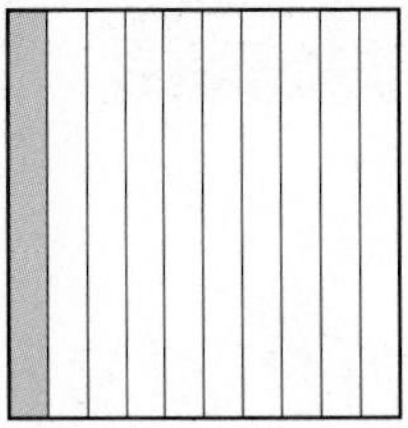

4. 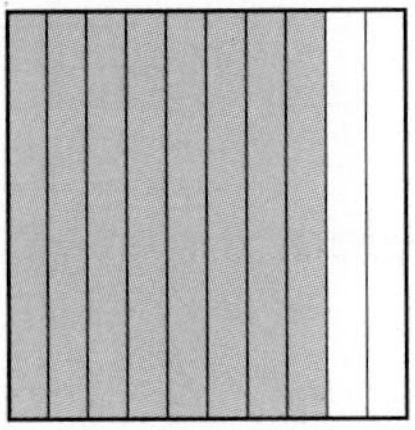   5. 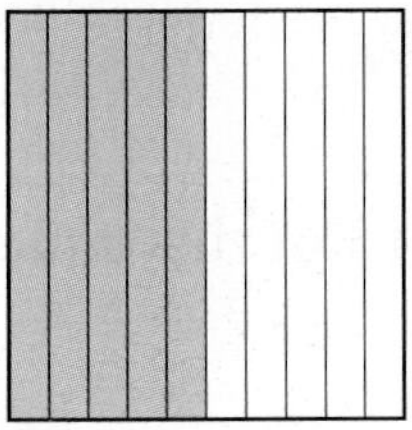   6.

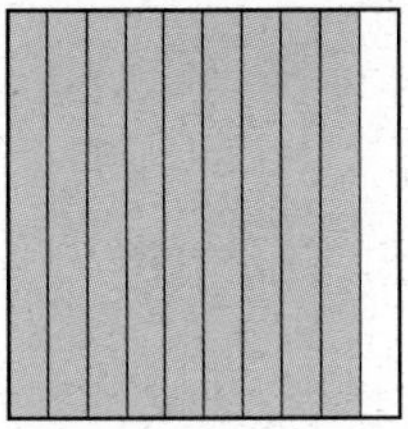

Example   This diagram shows one whole and six tenths.

We write this as 1.6.

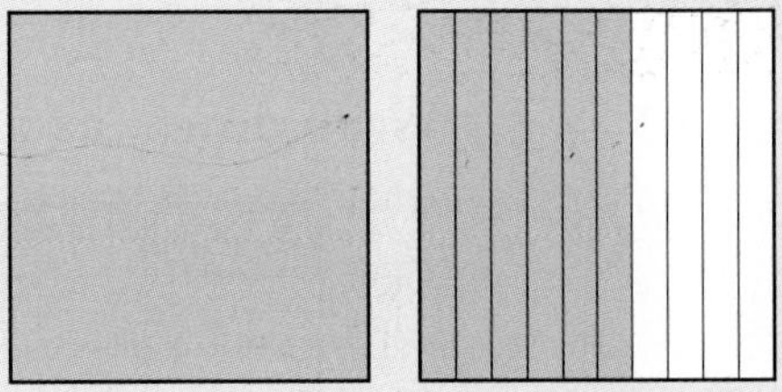

Exercise 2   Write down, as a decimal, what these diagrams show.

1. 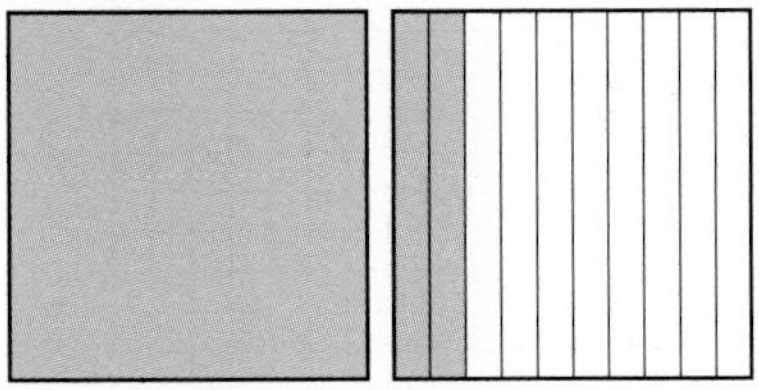   2.

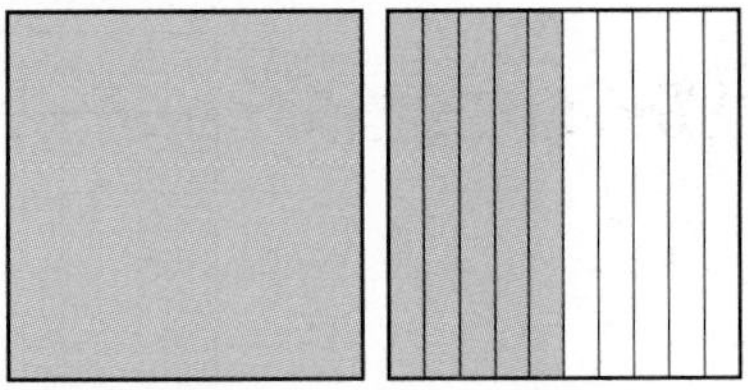

3.

4.

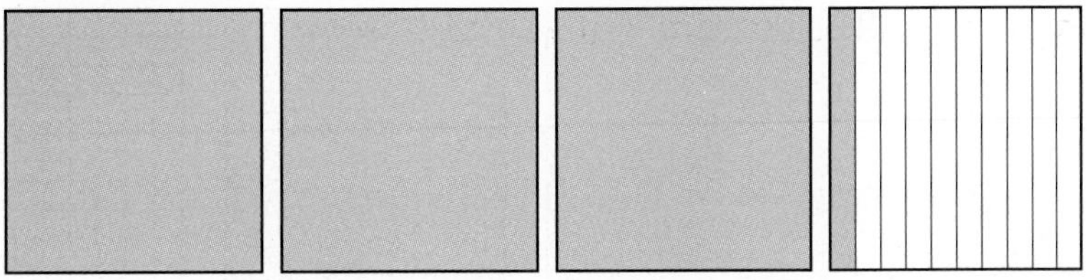

This square has been divided into one hundred parts.
Each part is one hundredth or $\frac{1}{100}$.

We can write $\frac{1}{100}$ as 0.01

$\frac{3}{100}$ as 0.03

$\frac{27}{100}$ as 0.27

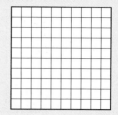

Example $\frac{13}{100}$ or 0.13 of this square is shaded.

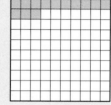

Exercise 3   Write down, as a decimal, how much is shaded.

1. 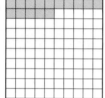   2. 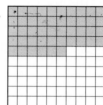   3.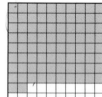

4. 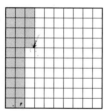   5. 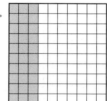   6.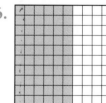

7.

8.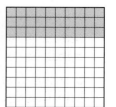

Example   6 and 4 tenths is written as 6.4.

5 and 3 tenths and 7 hundredths is written as 5.37.

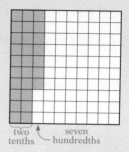

27 hundredths is 0.27.

This is the same as 2 tenths
and 7 hundredths.

two tenths — seven hundredths

Example   5 tenths and 2 hundredths is the same as 52 hundredths or $\frac{52}{100}$.

This is written as 0.52.

Exercise 4   Use a copy of this.
Fill it in.

	Fraction	Decimal
five tenths	$\frac{5}{10}$	0.5
seven tenths		
three hundredths		
three and fifty seven hundredths	$3\frac{57}{100}$	
two tenths and eight hundredths		
four tenths and six hundredths		
one and six tenths and four hundredths		
eight and nine tenths and one hundredth		
four and one tenth and eight hundredths		
nine and seven hundredths		
three and sixty hundredths		

Reading and writing decimals

We read 0.84 as zero point eight four.

56.32 is read as fifty six point three two.

29.04 is read as twenty nine point zero four.

Exercise 5

A Write down how these numbers are read.

1. 5.6   2. 4.3   3. 0.81   4. 0.78
5. 0.03   6. 24.6   7. 18.7   8. 10.05
9. 13.62   10. 15.07   11. 168.32   12. 327.01
13. 19.10   14. 23.60   15. 300.01

B Write these as decimals.

1. one point seven   2. one point six
3. five point eight three   4. seven point zero nine
5. six point zero three   6. nine point four three
7. thirty four point two one   8. eighty six point zero nine
9. fifty seven point nine nine

C

In 1995 over forty five point six eight million cars were made.
Write forty five point six eight as a decimal.

D There are 1.57 people in Britain for every TV set.
Write 1.57 in words.

E How do we read £16.54?
Are there any other decimals we read like money?

Puzzle

I am a decimal.
I have two digits before the decimal point.
I have two digits after the decimal point.
My first digit is smaller than my second digit.
My second digit is the same as my third digit.
My first digit is the same as my last digit.
My digits add up to eight.
What number am I?

Game for a group: GET THE POINT

You will need   pencil and paper

To play   • Choose a leader.

• The leader writes down a decimal number.

• The rest of the group have to find the number.
Take turns to ask the leader questions.
The leader can only answer Yes or No.

Example   Ben wrote this number.

5.03

Tim : Are there two digits after the point?		Ben : Yes
Ama : Are there two digits before the point?		Ben : No
Sue : Is there one digit before the point?		Ben : Yes
Max : Is the digit before the point less than 5?		Ben : No
Tim : Is it 5?		Ben : Yes
Ama : Is there a nought in the number?		Ben : Yes
Sue : Is the last digit bigger than 5?		Ben : No
Max : Is the last digit less than 3?		Ben : No
Tim : Is the last digit 3?		Ben : Yes
Ama : Is the number 5.03?		Ben : Yes

• The person who said the number is the new leader.

Homework/Review 1

A   What sweets would a person about to die like to have?

| $\underset{0.26}{\rule{0.6cm}{0.4pt}}$ | $\underset{1.4}{\rule{0.6cm}{0.4pt}}$ | $\underset{0.60}{\rule{0.6cm}{0.4pt}}$ | $\underset{0.04}{\rule{0.6cm}{0.4pt}}$ | $\overset{S}{\underset{0.4}{\rule{0.6cm}{0.4pt}}}$ | $\underset{1.44}{\rule{0.6cm}{0.4pt}}$ | $\underset{2.66}{\rule{0.6cm}{0.4pt}}$ | $\underset{0.04}{\rule{0.6cm}{0.4pt}}$ | $\underset{2.6}{\rule{0.6cm}{0.4pt}}$ | $\overset{S}{\underset{0.4}{\rule{0.6cm}{0.4pt}}}$ |

Use a copy of this box.
What decimal number do these show?

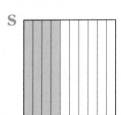

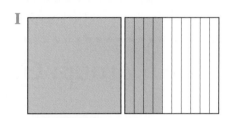

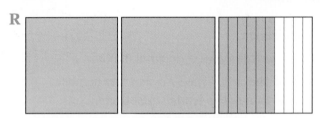

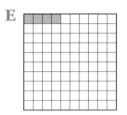

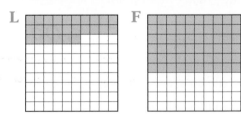

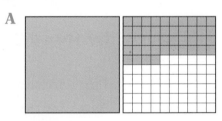

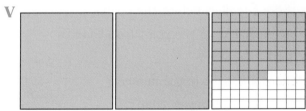

B   Write down how these numbers are read.
1.   8.3   2.   0.04   3.   0.92   4.   26.04

C   Write these as decimals.
1.   six point seven   2.   twenty eight point nine two
3.   five point zero one   4.   thirty six point zero nine

Adding and subtracting decimals

When we **add and subtract decimals** we line up the decimal points.

Example   3.12 + 42.71 is written as

$$\begin{array}{r} 3.12 \\ +\ 42.71 \\ \hline \end{array}$$

The decimal point in the answer is under the other decimal points.

We add or subtract as if the decimal point wasn't there.

Example   4.73 + 0.8 is

$$\begin{array}{r} 4.73 \\ +\ 0.8\ 0 \\ \hline 5.53 \end{array}$$

Put a zero to fill the gap.

3 hundredths + 0 hundredths = 3 hundredths.
7 tenths + 8 tenths = 15 tenths.
15 tenths is 1 one and 5 tenths.
Write down the 5.
Add the 1 one to the ones.
4 ones + 0 ones + 1 one = 5 ones.

Example   18.79 – 3.61 is

$$\begin{array}{r} 18.79 \\ -\ 3.61 \\ \hline 15.18 \end{array}$$

Example   29.04 – 13.63 is

$$\begin{array}{r} 2\ ^8 9.^1 04 \\ -\ 13.63 \\ \hline 15.41 \end{array}$$

4 – 3 = 1
We can't take 6 tenths from 0 tenths.
We make a one into 10 tenths.

Exercise 6   **A**   Use a copy of this.
Fill in the answers.

1. $\begin{array}{r}3.1\\+2.4\\\hline\end{array}$	**2.** $\begin{array}{r}6.3\\+2.4\\\hline\end{array}$	**3.** $\begin{array}{r}7.2\\+1.7\\\hline\end{array}$	**4.** $\begin{array}{r}5.3\\+4.3\\\hline\end{array}$
5. $\begin{array}{r}9.6\\+2.7\\\hline\end{array}$	**6.** $\begin{array}{r}6.8\\+2.5\\\hline\end{array}$	**7.** $\begin{array}{r}19.3\\+0.5\\\hline\end{array}$	**8.** $\begin{array}{r}2.34\\+8.9\\\hline\end{array}$
9. $\begin{array}{r}24.5\\+18.84\\\hline\end{array}$	**10.** $\begin{array}{r}16.09\\+6.3\\\hline\end{array}$	**11.** $\begin{array}{r}9.89\\+0.68\\\hline\end{array}$	**12.** $\begin{array}{r}0.04\\+23.69\\\hline\end{array}$

13.   4.32   14.   5.79   15.   17.34
        6.14   6.34   4.6
     + 5.31   + 7.86   + 12.07

B   Use a copy of this.
     Fill in the answers.

1.   9.7   2.   8.5   3.   12.8   4.   26.9
     − 6.3   − 2.1   − 7.5   − 14.8

5.   6.3   6.   12.4   7.   15.6   8.   25.51
     − 4.7   − 8.6   − 9.7   − 11.8

9.   34.86   10.   24.73   11.   84.35   12.   99.69
   − 16.32   − 17.91   − 12.13   − 37.59

C   Use a copy of this.
     Fill it in.

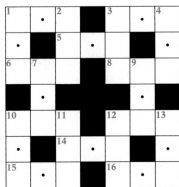

Across

1. 1.6 + 3.6
3. 2.9 + 2.5
5. 6.3 − 2.5
6. 78.5 + 45.5
8. 74.3 + 88.7
10. 87.2 + 93.8
12. 171.7 − 13.7
14. 13.9 − 5.7
15. 23.5 − 13.9
16. 35.5 − 27.6

Down

1. 3.7 + 1.4
2. 288.7 − 54.7
3. 324.9 + 256.1
4. 22.1 − 17.8
7. 9.5 − 6.7
9. 3.6 + 2.9
10. 16.6 − 14.7
11. 120.3 + 65.7
12. 89.4 + 25.1 + 12.5
13. 32.5 − 23.6

Example   79.2 − 3.68 is

$$
\begin{array}{r}
7\,9.\overset{8}{\cancel{2}}\overset{11}{\cancel{0}} \\
-\ \ 3.6\,8 \\
\hline
7\,5.5\,2
\end{array}
$$

← Put a zero to fill the gap.

We can't take 8 hundredths from 0 hundredths.

We make a tenth into 10 hundredths.

Exercise 7   Use a copy of this.
     Fill in the answers.

1.   84.3   2.   98.6   3.   84.2   4.   52.5
   − 12.14   − 37.59   − 27.39   − 39.38

5.   61.0   6.   49.5   7.   52.3
   − 39.36   − 26.94   − 29.54

Example Mary biked 0.8 km to Liz's house.
Then she biked 2.7 km to the shops.
How far did she bike altogether?

Answer We have to add 0.8 and 2.7.

$$\begin{array}{r} 0.8 \\ + \ 2.7 \\ \hline 3.5 \end{array}$$

She biked 3.5 km altogether.

Exercise 8   **A**   1. Ann had £6.84.
She was given £2.15.
How much did she have now?

2. Bob had £13.79.
He spent £6.35.
How much did he have now?

3. Chris had £26.58.
He was given £5.65.
How much did he have now?

4. Joyce had £19.43.
She spent £8.75.
How much did she have now?

B   1. Three classes sold sweets to make money.
This is what they got.

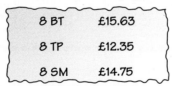

8 BT	£15.63
8 TP	£12.35
8 SM	£14.75

MINTS
5p each

Chocolate bars 50p

How much did the three classes make altogether?

2. Class 8BT spent £12.80 on a book for the library.
How much did they have left?

3. Class 8TP spent £6.90 on a present for a teacher.
How much did they have left?

C A piece of rope was cut into 3 bits.
They were 8.9 m, 7.6 m and 4.8 m long.

How long was the rope to start with?

D Carl and his cat weigh 48.3 kg.
Carl weighs 44.9 kg.

How much does the cat weigh?

Remember . . .

Magic squares

Whichever way you add them up you get
the same answer.

This magic square adds up to 5.4.

1.9	1.3	2.2
2.1	1.8	1.5
1.4	2.3	1.7

Exercise 9

Use a copy of this magic square.

Fill it in.

1.5	0.9	1.8
	1.4	

Exercise 10

This magic square must add to 5.4.

Find some ways of filling it in.

		1.3
	1.8	
2.3		

Puzzle

2.7	3	3.13	16	0.27	6.46	3.7

What is the biggest number you can make by
- adding two numbers from the box
- subtracting two numbers from the box?

What if we changed the word biggest to smallest?

Homework/Review 2

A **Why couldn't the tennis player light a fire?**

			A							
10.6	5.7	6.9	9.5	2.5	4.4	5.7		4.4	21.72	5.7

	A								A	
21.72	9.5	11.8		5.2	2.6	4.4	2.65		9.5	5.2	5.2

					A				
21.72	5.7	14.3		6.67	9.5	2.65	6.9	21.72	5.7	4.4

Use a copy of this box.

A	4.3 + 5.2 = 9.5		**D**	8.1 + 3.7		**C**	4.6 + 2.3
U	7.9 – 5.4		**L**	12.6 – 7.4		**B**	5.7 + 4.9
R	8.7 + 5.6		**O**	9.3 – 6.7		**S**	12.1 – 7.7
E	23.6 – 17.9		**H**	17.09 + 4.63		**T**	11.35 – 8.7
M	14.06 – 7.39						

B Karen had 3 pieces of wood.
They were 4.3 m, 2.6 m and 1.8 m long.
How long were they altogether?

C Misa needed £16.75 to buy some sunglasses.
She had saved £11.90.
How much more did she need?

Task

You have just won £100 to spend.
Write down a list of things you would like to buy.
Write down the cost of each.
Choose some things you would buy that add to exactly £100.

◀◀ CHAPTER REVIEW ◀◀

◀◀

Exercises 2
and 3 on
pages 151
and 152

A Write down, as a decimal, how much is shaded.

1.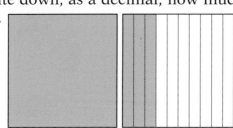

2.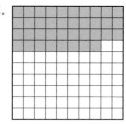

◀◀

Exercise 4
on page 153

B Use a copy of this.
Fill it in.

	Fraction	Decimal
three tenths		
ten and six tenths		
seventy nine hundredths		
three tenths and nine hundredths		
six and eighty five hundredths		
four and one tenth and one hundredth		

◀◀

Exercise 5
on page 154

C 1. Brad was 1.57 m tall.
Write down how we read 1.57.

2. Brad wrote his mother's height in words.
My mother is one point six four metres tall.
Write this height as a decimal.

◀◀

Exercises
6 and 7 on
pages 157
and 158

D Use a copy of this.

1.
$$4.6 \\ + 5.2$$

2.
$$6.7 \\ + 3.8$$

3.
$$15.7 \\ - 6.3$$

4.
$$4.86 \\ - 2.43$$

5.
$$8.43 \\ - 6.78$$

6.
$$14.73 \\ + 10.98$$

7.
$$11.7 \\ - 5.06$$

8.
$$53.6 \\ - 29.78$$

◀◀

Exercise 8
on page 159

E 1. Jon had £9.87.
He was given £3.64.
How much did he have then?

2. Mary had £7.64.
She spent £4.97.
How much did she have then?

Quick Test 4

A Mick went on a hike.
He used this map.

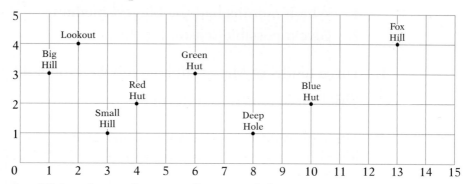

1. Write down the coordinates of these.
    Red Hut   Blue Hut   Fox Hill

2. What will you find at these coordinates?
    (6, 3)   (1, 3)   (2, 4)   (8, 1)

3. Use a copy of the map.
    Put a pool at (11, 4).
    Put a big tree at (14, 2).

B These are the distances of the hikes Mick has been on.
12 km   17 km   24 km   18 km   26 km   15 km   12 km

1. What is the median distance of the hikes?
2. What is the mode of these distances?

C Mick asked his friends what hikes they had done.

Shana	17 km 19 km 27 km
Luke	19 km 15 km 29 km
Steve	21 km 27 km 19 km
Lucy	19 km 22 km 30 km

Mick wrote all the distances in order.
   15 km, 17 km, 19 km, 19 km, ...

1. Copy and finish Mick's list.
2. What is the median distance?
3. What is the mode of the distances?

D Mick's hiking club drew this table.

January–March	April–June	July–September	October–December
median distance = 19 km	median distance = 24 km	median distance = 29 km	median distance = 15 km

1. Which months had the biggest median?
2. Give a possible reason for this.

E Three tenths of Mick's hiking club went on a hike.

Write three tenths as a decimal.

F The club record for the biggest distance hiked in a day was thirty eight point seven two kilometres.

Write thirty eight point seven two as a decimal.

G These are the bills of some people in the hiking club.

Use a copy of this.

Fill in the answers.

1.
```
   2.64
+  8.2
£ _____
```

2.
```
   0.56
+ 22.71
£ _____
```

3.
```
  16.85
+ 12.96
£ _____
```

4.
```
   5.78
   6.37
+  7.88
£ _____
```

5.
```
  25.82
- 11.6
£ _____
```

6.
```
  98.75
-  4.23
£ _____
```

7.
```
  84.23
-  3.96
£ _____
```

8.
```
  63.0
-  8.57
£ _____
```

H The hiking club had a stall to raise money.

This is what they got.

Money raised	
cakes	£36.55
sweets	£23.89
apples	£15.76

1. How much did they get altogether?
2. They spent £17.95 on maps.
   How much did they have left?

Sliding, Turning, Reflecting

Making patterns.............................

 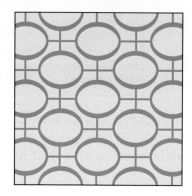 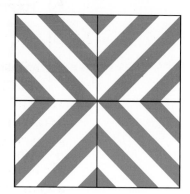

How have these patterns been made?

Write a sentence about each.

Sliding and turning

Remember . . .

This heart has been **slid**.

These hearts have been **turned**.

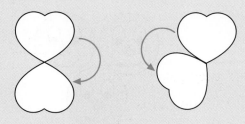

Exercise 1   **A**   The hearts on these have been slid or turned.

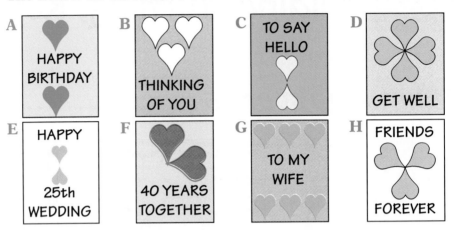

1. Which cards have hearts that have been slid?

2. Which cards have hearts that have been turned?

B   These patterns have been made by sliding or turning the shape on the left.

Write sliding or turning for each one.

1.

2.

3.

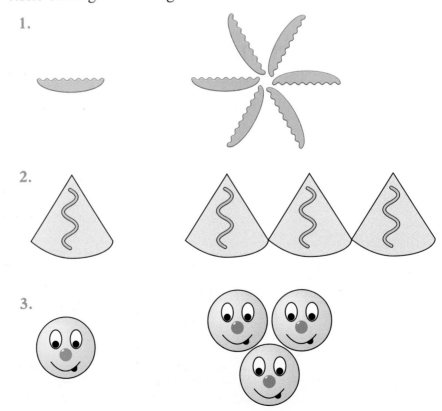

Reflecting in a mirror line

Task

You will need a mirror

Put the mirror along the dashed line.

What do you see in the mirror?

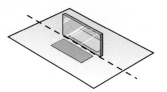

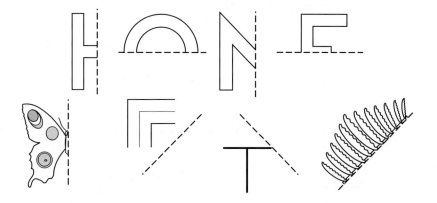

Example This shape has been reflected in the mirror line.

mirror line

To reflect a shape in a mirror line you can use a mirror.

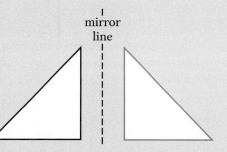

shape to be reflected

hold mirror on mirror line

draw what you see

Example   Reflect this shape in the mirror line.

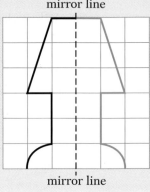

mirror line

Answer   We use a mirror or tracing paper
           to draw the reflection.

mirror line

Exercise 2   Use a copy of this.
                  Reflect these shapes in the mirror line.

1.
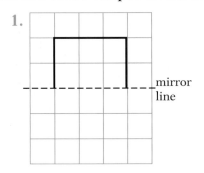
mirror
line

2.
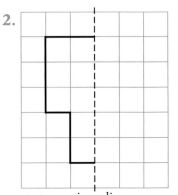
mirror line

3.
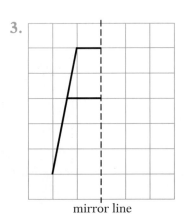
mirror line

4.
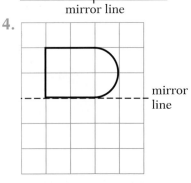
mirror
line

5.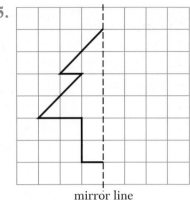

6.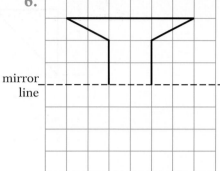

Example   Reflect this shape in the mirror line.

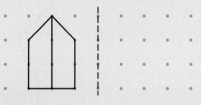

Answer   Use a mirror or tracing paper to help draw this reflection.

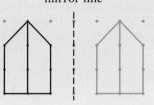

Exercise 3   Use a copy of this.

Reflect these shapes in the mirror line.

1.   mirror line

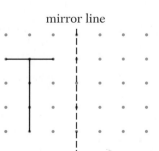

2.   mirror line

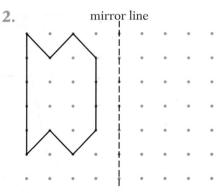

3.

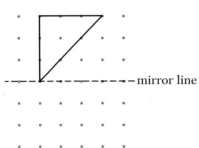

mirror line

4.

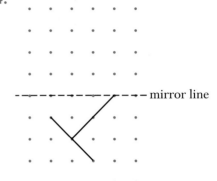

mirror line

5.

mirror line

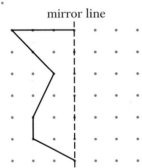

6.

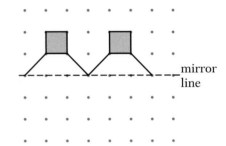

mirror line

7.

mirror line

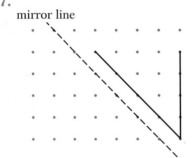

8.

mirror line

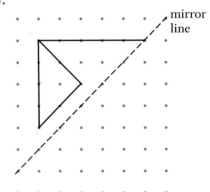

9. mirror line

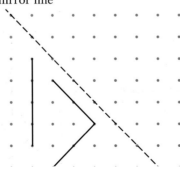

Exercise 4 **A** Which of these show reflections in the mirror line?

The dashed lines are mirror lines.

1.

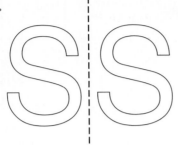

2.

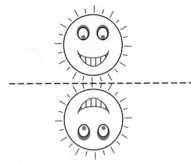

3.

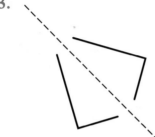

4.

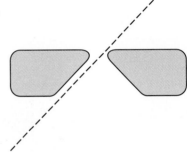

5.

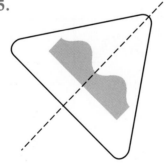

6.

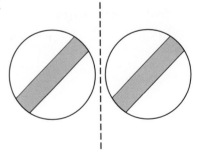

B Are these true?

Write **yes** or **no**.

1. **B** is a reflection of **A**.
2. **D** is a reflection of **A**.
3. **C** is a reflection of **B**.
4. **C** is a reflection of **D**.

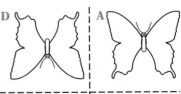
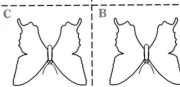

Sometimes we make reflections in two mirror lines.

We begin with a shape.

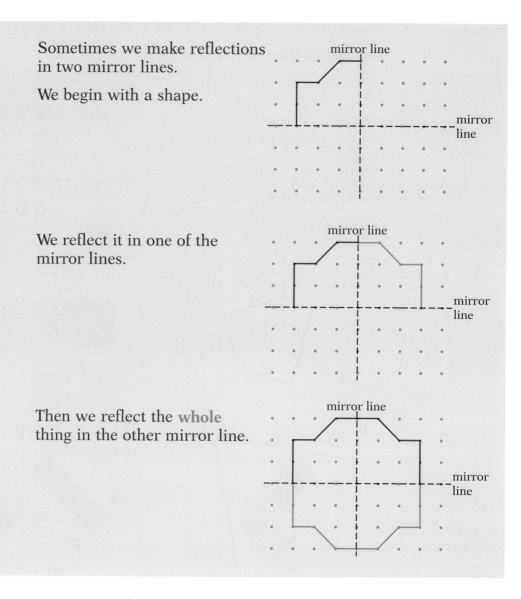

We reflect it in one of the mirror lines.

Then we reflect the **whole** thing in the other mirror line.

Exercise 5

Use a copy of this.
Reflect the shape in one mirror line to make a pattern.
Then reflect the whole pattern in the other mirror line.

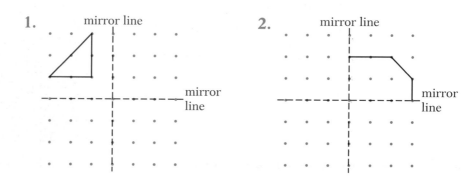

3.

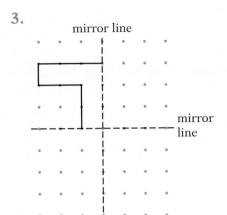

mirror line

mirror line

4.

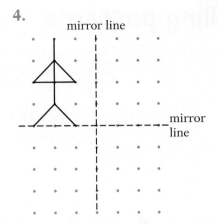

mirror line

mirror line

5.

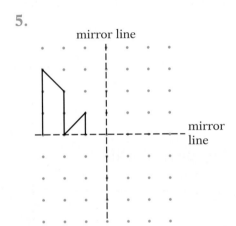

mirror line

mirror line

6.

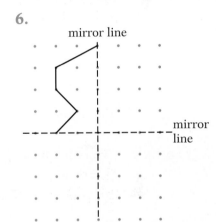

mirror line

mirror line

Game for 2 players: BE MY MIRROR

To play
- Choose who will start.
- This person makes slow movements with their hands.
- The other player must be their 'mirror' and make movements to match.
- If this player makes a mistake, swap over.

Tiling patterns

We can fit some shapes together so there are no gaps.

Examples   These tiles fit together
with no gaps.

These ones leave gaps.

Sometimes the shape has to be turned or reflected so it fits
together.

Example   We can make a tiling pattern with
this shape.

Tiling pattern

Exercise 6   Use a copy of this.

A   Joe chose this shaped tile.

Finish Joe's tiling pattern.

B Brenda chose this shaped tile.

Finish Brenda's tiling pattern.

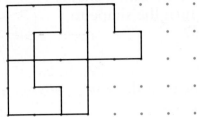

C Ravi chose this shaped tile.

Finish Ravi's tiling pattern.

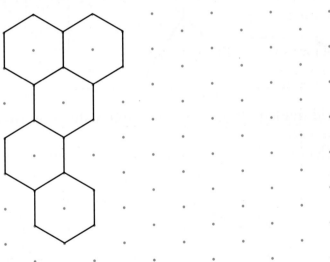

Exercise 7   Use square dot paper.

1. Use this shape to make a
    tiling pattern.

2. Use this shape to make a
    tiling pattern.

    Try and find more than one way of making a tiling pattern
    with this shape.

Homework/Review

A   Cindy made a pattern with a shape.
Did she slide or turn the shape to
make the pattern?

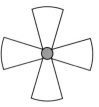

B   Pat made patterns by reflecting shapes in a mirror line.
Use a copy of this.
Reflect these in the mirror line.

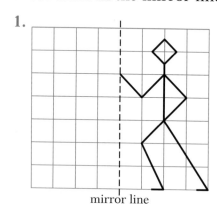

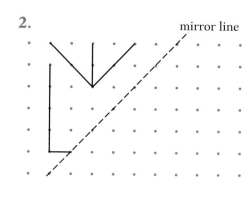

C   Farid made patterns by reflecting a shape in two mirror lines.
Use a copy of this.
Reflect the shape in one mirror line to make a pattern.
Then reflect the whole pattern in the other mirror line.

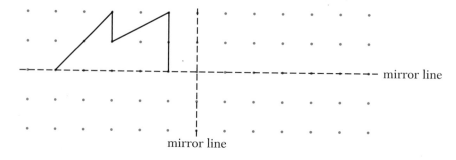

D   Use a copy of this.
Finish Enid's tiling pattern.

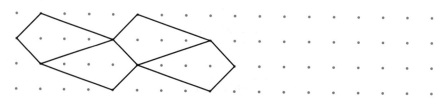

Puzzle

Use a copy of this.
Cut out these four shapes.

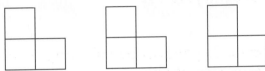

Use your four shapes
to tile this shape.

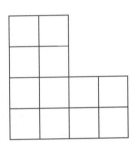

◀◀ CHAPTER REVIEW ◀◀

◀◀

Exercises 2
and 3 on
pages 168
and 169

A   Use a copy of this.

Paul made patterns for his wall by reflecting shapes.
Reflect these in the mirror line.

1.

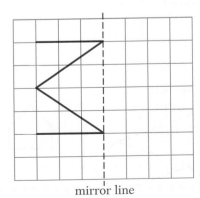

mirror line

2.

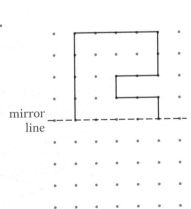

mirror
line

Exercise 4
on page 171

B   Which of these do *not* show reflections in the mirror line?
The dashed line is the mirror line.

1. 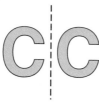   2.    3.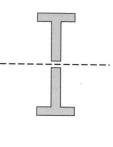

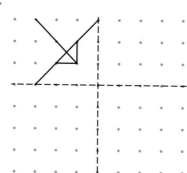
Exercise 5
on page 172

C   Use a copy of this.
Reflect the shape in one mirror line to make a pattern.
Then reflect the whole pattern in the other mirror line.

1.   2.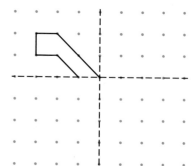

Exercise 6
on page 174

D   Use a copy of this.

1.   Gary chose this shaped tile.
Finish Gary's tiling pattern.

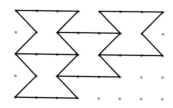

2.   Use square dot paper.
Use this shape to make
a tiling pattern.

14 Rounding and Estimating

Sensible sayings...

My train leaves in 31 minutes and 26 seconds

I am twelve years, two months, five days and sixteen hours old

I am 163 cm and 4 mm tall

Are these sentences sensible? Why not?

What could each have said instead?

Rounding

Sometimes we are asked to round to the nearest ten or nearest hundred.

Remember

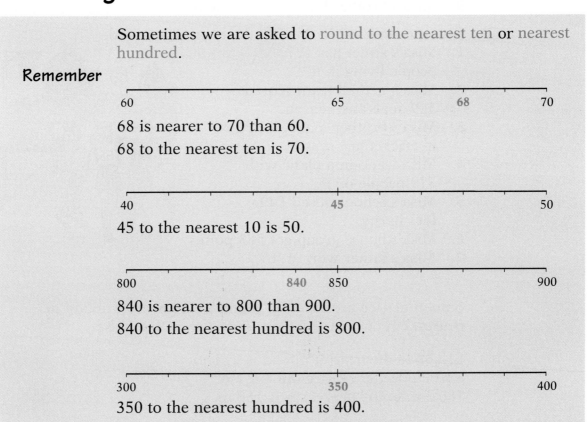

60   65   68   70

68 is nearer to 70 than 60.

68 to the nearest ten is 70.

40   45   50

45 to the nearest 10 is 50.

800   840   850   900

840 is nearer to 800 than 900.

840 to the nearest hundred is 800.

300   350   400

350 to the nearest hundred is 400.

Exercise 1   **A**   Give these to the nearest ten.
1. 48   2. 59   3. 71   4. 65
5. 95   6. 163   7. 146   8. 235
9. 587   10. 611   11. 1741   12. 4812
13. 5329   14. 7927

B   Give these to the nearest hundred.
1. 190   2. 204   3. 516   4. 793
5. 564   6. 450   7. 850   8. 586
9. 418   10. 949   11. 1345   12. 2910
13. 3555   14. 5962

C   Give the amounts in these to the nearest ten.
1. Misa's class has 29 pupils.
2. Misa's mother has 12 cousins.
3. Misa has £69 in the bank.
4. Misa's school has 479 pupils.
5. Misa weighs 118 pounds.
6. Misa's family got 104 Christmas cards.
7. Misa's stereo cost £325.
8. Misa's aunt lives 468 km away.
9. Misa's brother has £1276 in the bank.

D   Give the amounts in these to the nearest hundred.
1. Misa's street has 127 people living in it.
2. Misa's netball team scored 369 goals this season.
3. Misa's brother made 686 runs in cricket last season.
4. Misa went on a plane with 379 people on it.
5. Misa's school raised £496 for charity.
6. Misa's house group got 583 points.
7. Misa's father won £1269.

Sometimes we are asked to round to the nearest pound or nearest cm or nearest kg or nearest something else.

Examples   £12.69 to the nearest pound is £13.
8.63 cm to the nearest cm is 9 cm.
186.3 m to the nearest m is 186 m.

Exercise 2

A Round these to the nearest £.

1. £2.04	2. £6.86	3. £10.74	4. £16.05
5. £24.63	6. £33.69	7. £17.99	8. £18.20
9. £127.94	10. £189.29	11. £8.50	12. £10.50
13. £89.50	14. £126.40	15. £783.50	16. £426.45

B Round these to the nearest kg.

1. 5.2 kg	2. 7.8 kg	3. 16.4 kg	4. 18.5 kg
5. 29.9 kg	6. 153.6 kg	7. 127.5 kg	8. 386.2 kg
9. 1827.5 kg	10. 5862.8 kg		

C Round these to the nearest m.

1. 33.2 m	2. 47.1 m	3. 86.8 m	4. 127.4 m
5. 326.5 m	6. 852.7 m	7. 831.4 m	8. 762.5 m
9. 180.9 m	10. 100.3 m		

D 1. Lisa weighs 44.6 kg.
Round this to the nearest kg.

2. Anna's handspan is 16.3 cm.
Round this to the nearest cm.

3. Dylan's house is 5.7 km from the school.
Round this to the nearest km.

4. Colin walked 10.7 km one weekend.
Round this to the nearest km.

5. Julie's fingernail is 9.2 mm across.
Round this to the nearest mm.

6. Bob's boat is 16.4 m long.
Round this to the nearest m.

7. Joyce's fence is 568.5 m long.
Round this to the nearest m.

Sometimes we aren't told what to round to.
We have to round to a sensible amount.

Example   Sarah has £69.83 to spend on a stereo.
We could say that Sarah has nearly £70 to spend.

Example   Bob won £687.21.
We could say one of these.
  Bob won about £687.
  Bob won nearly £690.
  Bob won nearly £700.
All of these would be sensible.

Exercise 3   What would be a sensible amount to go in the gap?

1. Milltown School raised £698.92 for charity.
    The school has raised nearly _____.

2. John is 11 years 10 months and 26 days.
    John is nearly _____.

3. Ben had £986.95 in the bank.
    Ben had nearly _____.

4. Rita ran 879 metres to her friend's house.
    Rita ran about _____.

5. Ama drank 186 m*l* of juice for breakfast.
    Ama drank about _____.

6. Farid spent £487.92 on Christmas presents.
    Farid spent about _____ on these.

7. Sam spent 28 minutes and 52 seconds on his homework.
    Sam spent about _____ on his homework.

8. Helen bought a coat for £204.85.
    The coat cost about _____.

9. Dean's plane leaves in 3 hours 33 minutes.
    Dean's plane leaves in about _____.

Homework/Review 1

A **What do you get if you put hot water down a rabbit hole?**

	O					O		
———	———	———		———	———	———	———	———
300	90	1800		1860	130	90	140	140

———	———	———	———	———	———	———
80	120	150	150	1700	200	140

Use a copy of this box.
Round these to what is given in the brackets.

O 86 (nearest ten)
R 125 (nearest ten)
U 122 (nearest ten)
B 75 (nearest ten)
H 286 (nearest hundred)
N 145 (nearest ten)

E 168 (nearest hundred)
I 1721 (nearest hundred)
T 1794 (nearest hundred)
C 1864 (nearest ten)
S 139 (nearest ten)

B This tells you all about Fred.
Round all the numbers to the nearest £, cm, kg, or mm.

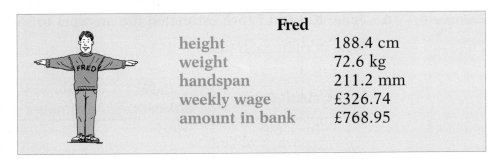

	Fred
height	188.4 cm
weight	72.6 kg
handspan	211.2 mm
weekly wage	£326.74
amount in bank	£768.95

C What would be a sensible amount to go in the gap?

1. Tina bought a car for £879.62.
   Tina paid about ——— for her car.

2. Deri bought a stereo for £279.65.
   He paid about ——— for it.

3. Emma spent £687.92 on her holiday.
   Her holiday cost nearly ——— .

Estimating

Estimating an answer gives us an idea of what it should be.

Example   Ben had £28.

He was given another £19.

Ben worked out he now had £37.

How can you tell Ben is wrong without doing the calculation?

Answer   We can estimate how much Ben has.

£28 is about £30.

£19 is about £20.

£30 + £20 = £50.

Ben has about £50, so £37 is wrong.

Exercise 4   **A**   Jane, Kate and Josh estimated the answers to some calculations.
Who is right each time?

Calculation	Jane's estimate	Kate's estimate	Josh's estimate
1. £58 + £19	£80	£70	£60
2. £51 + £48	£80	£90	£100
3. £17 + £69	£70	£80	£90
4. £79 − £21	£50	£60	£70
5. 82 m − 51 m	30 m	40 m	20 m
6. 59 cm + 12 cm	70 cm	80 cm	60 cm
7. 78 km + 31 km	100 km	90 km	110 km
8. 110 mm − 51 mm	50 mm	60 mm	70 mm
9. 81 − 49	20	40	30
10. 84 − 29	50	40	60

B   1.   Jane had £59.
She was given another £48.⌋
Jane said 'Now I have £127'.
Explain how you can tell Jane is wrong without doing the calculation.

2.   Kate had £81.
She spent £49.
She wanted to buy a dress for £25.
Estimate to see if she had enough.

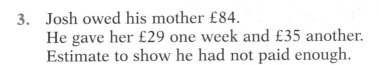

3.   Josh owed his mother £84.
He gave her £29 one week and £35 another.
Estimate to show he had not paid enough.

Example   Mandy bought 8 hair ties for £0.95 each.
She was asked to pay £9.55.
Show why this is wrong without doing the calculation.

Answer   £0.95 is about £1.
8 × £1 = £8
So she should have to pay a little less than £8.

Exercise 5   **A**   Estimate to show that these are wrong.

1.   £3.99 × 5 = £15
2.   £5.99 × 4 = £20.96
3.   £4.82 × 4 = £30.28
4.   89 p × 5 = £6.50
5.   £6.85 × 7 = £45.95
6.   £3.89 × 9 = £32.01
7.   £6.69 × 4 = £23.76
8.   £10.06 × 4 = £38.24
9.   £6.03 × 6 = £38.18
10.   £9.15 × 8 = £70.44

B   Explain why each of these was
asked to pay the wrong amount.
Do not do the calculation.

1.   Carl bought 6 mugs for
£2.99 each.
He was asked to pay £18.94.

2.   Brenda bought 5 bags of fudge for £1.95 each.
She was asked to pay £8.75.

3.   Shana bought 7 bags of small cakes for £3.10 a bag.
She was asked to pay £24.80.

Example   Jim knew the amount to pay on this
bill was wrong. He had made an
estimate of what he had to pay.
He thought

'£4.10 is about £4,

£2.86 is about £3,

so I have to pay about £7'.

Bill

meal	£4.10
pudding	£2.86
To pay	£8.96

Exercise 6

A   Show that each of these bills has been added up wrongly.
Do not do the calculation.

1.
CINEMA

2 Adults	£8.40
4 Children	£12.00
To pay	£30.00

2.
WONDER TOURS

2 × By night	£38.20
3 × Zoo	£42.00
To pay	£50.00

3.
CAFE EATS

Cake	£1.40
Drink	£0.85
To pay	£4.25

4.
BROWN'S

Cups	£4.90
Plates	£7.16
To pay	£11.06

5.
CAR PARTS

Pump	£11.99
Wipers	£7.99
VAT	£3.50
To pay	£20.48

6.
DINNER 42

Main	£8.20
Main	£9.90
Desert	£6.90
	£35.00

7.
SOUNDS

Stereo	£149
CDs	£51
To pay	£304

8.
Jewellers

Earrings	£9.99
Bracelet	£4.00
Necklace	£4.99
To pay	£28.98

B   Estimate about how much these bills will be.

1.
SPARE PARTS

Wheel	£16.87
Cog	£5.09
To pay	

2.
SKATING

2 Adults	£9.80
3 Children	£7.80
To pay	

3.
Machines

Phone	£50.10
Fax	£279.60
To pay	

Homework/Review 2

A Estimate to show that these are not right.

1. £18 + £39 = £47
2. £69 + £21 = £80
3. £57 − £29 = £18
4. £39 − £12 = £17

B Paul and Vera went shopping.

1. Paul had £29.
   He spent £18.
   Did he have enough left to buy a watch for £17?

   Estimate to check.

2. Vera bought 6 books at this sale.

   She was asked to pay £19.70.

   Show that this is wrong without
   doing the calculation.

ALL SALE
BOOKS
£2.95

3. Paul and Vera had lunch.

   Show, without doing the
   calculation, that this bill
   has been added up wrongly.

RICK's CAFÉ

£2.80

£3.25

£1.95

£10.00

C Estimate about how much these bills are.

1.

   BOOKS

   Red   £15.80

   Blue   £19.95

   To pay _____

2.

   PARTIES

   Food   £78.20

   Plates £12.10

   To pay _____

3.

   HIRE

   Ladder £12.95

   Cleaner £78.20

   To pay _____

◀◀ CHAPTER REVIEW ◀◀

◀◀

Exercise 1
on page 180

A Give the amounts in these to the nearest ten.

1. Misa's dog weighs 38 kg.
2. Misa's foot is 118 mm long.
3. Misa is 163 cm tall.

◀◀

Exercise 1
on page 180

B Give the amounts in these to the nearest hundred.

1. Misa's father won £324.
2. Misa's bike cost £289.
3. Misa's grandmother lives 369 miles away.

◀◀

Exercise 2
on page 181

C Round these to what is in the brackets.

1. £5.19 (nearest £)   2. 17.6 kg (nearest kg)
3. 127.8 cm (nearest cm)   4. 396.4 mm (nearest mm)

◀◀

Exercise 3
on page 182

D What would be a sensible amount to go in the gap?

1. Hill School spent £896.27 on a computer.
   The school spent about _____ on the computer.

2. Sam's model plane is 298.7 mm long.
   It is nearly _____ mm long.

◀◀

Exercise 4
on page 184

E £69 + £22

Jane estimated the answer to this as £80.
Kate estimated it was £90.
Josh estimated it was £70.
Who was right?

◀◀

Exercise 5
on page 185

F Mary bought 8 books of stamps at £1.90 each.
She was asked to pay £12.20.

How can you tell, without doing the
calculation, that this is wrong?

◀◀

Exercise 6
on page 186

G Show, without doing the
calculation, that this bill
has been added up wrongly.

JEFF'S CYCLES

Helmet	£9.99
Light	£3.99
	£14.98

Using the Calculator

Mistakes ···

38 + 52

Karen got 63 as the answer. Is she right?

How could Karen check her answer?

Think of two ways.

Using the calculator

Remember . . .

58 + 64 is keyed as `5` `8` `+` `6` `4` `=`

276 ÷ 12 is keyed as `2` `7` `6` `÷` `1` `2` `=`

When you use the calculator **always** check your answer.

Ways to check your answer

- Do the calculation again.

  `5` `7` `+` `6` `8` `=` $\boxed{125.}$

  Check again `5` `7` `+` `6` `8` `=` $\boxed{125.}$

• Do the calculation a different way.

Check by keying

| 6 | 8 | + | 5 | 7 | = |

Will this work for subtracting?

What about dividing?

• Use the answer to check.

Check by keying

| 1 | 2 | 5 | − | 6 | 8 | = | 57.

Exercise 1   Check the answers to these in 2 ways.
If it is wrong, write down the right answer.

1. 27 + 64 = 92   2. 53 × 61 = 2333
3. 60 ÷ 15 = 4   4. 18 × 21 = 278
5. 435 ÷ 5 = 87   6. 591 − 377 = 241
7. 83 × 42 = 186

Exercise 2   Use a calculator to find the answers to these.

A
1. 71 + 86   2. 94 − 59   3. 24 × 32
4. 592 ÷ 16   5. 186 + 97   6. 384 − 179
7. 45 × 17   8. 900 ÷ 36   9. 987 − 658
10. 35 × 47   11. 386 + 279   12. 1620 ÷ 45
13. 55 × 79   14. 384 + 1621   15. 3672 ÷ 51
16. 1843 − 264   17. 3591 ÷ 63   18. 47 × 61
19. 4320 − 686   20. 483 + 1471   21. 9862 − 7314
22. 2800 ÷ 56   23. 17 × 91   24. 5041 + 6309
25. 89 × 29   26. 156 × 21

B
1. 7 + 14 + 23   2. 111 + 117 + 29
3. 325 + 131 + 215   4. 189 − 27 − 64
5. 378 − 164 − 86   6. 527 − 329 − 51
7. 7 × 9 × 16   8. 8 × 24 × 31
9. 25 × 31 × 6   10. 583 + 261 + 316
11. 17 × 19 × 38   12. 586 − 314 − 124
13. 12 × 52 × 14

C Use a copy of this crossnumber.
Fill it in.

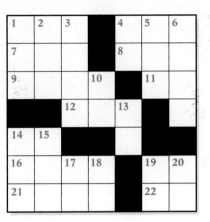

Across	Down
1. 17×21	1. $972 - 637$
4. $1093 - 834$	2. 5×111
7. 51×7	3. 311×25
8. $82 + 89$	4. $399 \div 19$
9. 136×41	5. 36×16
11. $1428 \div 21$	6. 135×68
12. 23×25	10. $3618 \div 54$
14. $3444 \div 41$	13. $780 \div 15$
16. $3826 + 2147$	14. $686 + 167$
19. $1344 \div 16$	15. $225 + 271$
21. 56×65	17. $753 - 679$
22. $4928 \div 154$	18. $1680 \div 56$
	19. $1339 - 1256$
	20. $1764 \div 42$

If you turn your calculator upside down, some numbers turn into words.

Example 335 is

$$335.$$

Upside down it reads

$$SEE$$

What word does 5317 turn into?

Exercise 3 **A** Do these calculations.
Turn your calculator upside down.
What words have you made?

1. 331×3
2. $7098 \div 21$
3. 1421×5
4. 67×5
5. $6523 + 1215$
6. $5069 - 563$
7. 4759×12
8. $1992 - 1259$

B Do these calculations in order.
Turn the calculator upside down.
Write down the words.
What message do you get?

$1904 \div 56$ $4005 + 1330$ $15\,469 \times 5$ $5606 - 4896$

In the next exercise you have to work out if you need to add, subtract, multiply or divide.

Exercise 4 · **A** **1.** Jane wrote down how much she drank in a day.

Drink	Amount
Juice	200 ml
Water	150 ml
Tea	150 ml
Water	200 ml
Juice	250 ml

How much did Jane drink altogether?

2. Jane's brother drank 1450 ml on Monday.
On Tuesday he drank 1986 ml.
How much more did he drink on Tuesday?

B **1.** These t-shirts cost £12 each.
The school bought 72 of them.
How much did this cost altogether?

2. Another school spent £1248 on t-shirts.
They each cost £12.
How many did they buy?

3. Banks School spent £2196 on t-shirts.
Later in the year they spent another £1644 on them.
How much did they spend altogether?

4. Riverdale School spent £5832 on t-shirts.
They sent some back and got £1068 back.
How much had they spent then?

C Work out the amount to pay.

1.

Dress for Best	
shirt	£89
skirt	£164
To pay	_____

2.

Dress for Best	
track pant	£34
handbag	£152
To pay	_____

D   This shows how much water Rob's house uses for some things.

14 *l* each flush   **80 *l*** each load   **96 *l*** for a 10-
minute shower   **5 *l*** to wash
hands

This is how many times these were done in Rob's house each week.

toilet flushed	146 times
washing clothes	4 loads
10-minute showers	18
hands washed	186 times

How much water was used altogether in Rob's house for each
of these?

1.   flushing the toilet   2.   washing clothes
3.   showers   4.   washing hands

E   Jane could write her name 21 times in one minute.

1.   How many times could she write it in an hour?
2.   How many times could she write it in a day?
3.   Work out how many times you can write your name in a
     minute, an hour and a day.

Investigation

The **6** on Penny's calculator was
not working.
She needed to calculate 26 + 72.
She said 26 is 24 + 2.
She pressed this to get the answer.

2 4 + 2 + 7 2 =

Work out how to calculate these on Penny's calculator.
36 + 51,   76 + 129,   52 × 6,   23 × 6,   16 × 23,   86 − 12

Game for 2 players: CRICKET

You will need   a calculator each

a card like this

Start	End	Ball 1	Ball 2	Ball 3	Ball 4	Ball 5	Number of balls
20	68						
89	21						
13	126						

To play
- Put the start number into your calculator.
- You must try and get the end number with the smallest number of balls.
- For each ball you can use **+** **−** **×** and **÷** and **one** of these keys **1** **2** **3** **4** **5** **6** **7** **8** **9**

Example

Start	End	Ball 1	Ball 2	Ball 3	Ball 4	Ball 5	Number of balls
20	68	20 × 2 = 40	40 × 2 = 80	80 − 9 = 71	71 − 3 = 68		4

- The player who uses the smallest number of balls each time gets 5 points.
- The player with the most points wins.
- You can play more games by making up your own **Start** and **End** numbers.

Puzzle

Key in the last 4 digits of your telephone number. Then key

× **2** **=**

+ **5** **=**

× **5** **0** **=**

− **6** **1** **5** **=**

+ **your age** **=**

+ **3** **6** **5** **=**

What do you get on the screen?

Homework/Review 1

A Use a calculator to find the answers to these.
Turn the calculator upside down.
What words have you made?

1. 15×23
2. $8782 - 704$
3. 9015×5
4. $40\ 131 \div 7$
5. 3849×15

B **What happened to the boy who listened to the match?**

$\frac{H}{152}$	$\overline{12\ 956}$		$\overline{280}$	$\overline{2268}$	$\overline{56}$	$\overline{29}$	$\overline{162}$
$\frac{H}{152}$	$\overline{3692}$	$\overline{5527}$		$\overline{12\ 956}$	$\overline{106}$	$\overline{56}$	

Use a copy of this box.
Use a calculator to find the answers to these.

H $69 + 83 = 152$ **A** $14 + 29 + 63$ **T** $486 - 324$
I 52×71 **U** 12×189 **N** $1044 \div 36$
S $962 + 4565$ **B** $389 - 62 - 47$ **R** $4984 \div 89$
E 79×164

C

CDs
£11

Signed picture
£117

Stereo
CD player
£289

Work out how much these would cost.

1. a CD and a picture
2. a CD player and a picture
3. 5 CDs
4. 3 CD players

D Jan used 12 litres of petrol each time she drove to her mother's house.
How much petrol would she use for 16 visits?

Decimals on the calculator

Remember . . .

Always check your answer.
When keying decimals be careful to get the decimal point in the right place.

56.7 + 0.23 is keyed as   **5** **6** **·** **7** **+** **0** **·** **2** **3**

Do we get the same answer if we key   **5** **6** **·** **7** **+** **·** **2** **3** ?

Exercise 5

A Use your calculator to find the answers to these.

1. $2.3 + 6.8$
2. $3.8 + 6.84$
3. $5.73 + 0.39$
4. $8.79 - 3.2$
5. $26.83 - 17.5$
6. 5.3×4
7. 2.4×6
8. $9.2 \div 4$
9. $18 \div 3.6$
10. 5.7×8
11. $32.6 - 17.93$
12. 1.45×7
13. $15.3 \div 6$
14. $4.14 \div 1.8$
15. 39.63×42.1
16. $10.576\ 65 \div 2.1$
17. 5.73×12.68

B Use a copy of these.
Fill in the missing numbers.

+	1.6	2.7	0.9
8.63			
0.79			
14.63			

×	1.2	3.6	0.8
5			
4.6			
0.9			

C Use a copy of this.
Start at the top.
Finish at any square along the bottom.

You may move ↓ or → or ← but not ↑ or ↘ or ↙ or ↖ or ↗

START

		2.01				
	2.07	2.4	2.13			
	2.09	2.19	2.03	2.18	2.13	
2.31	2.24	2.04	2.15	2.16	2.01	2.04

You can't go to a square more than once.
Find the path that adds to the biggest number.

Remember . . .

85 p is £0.85

Example   To find the cost of 3 kg of carrots at 85 p a kg we key

| 3 | × | 0 | · | 8 | 5 | = | to get

$$2.55$$

The answer is £2.55.

Exercise 6   **A**   Find the cost of these.

1. 2 kg of apples at £1.05 a kg

2. 1.2 kg of bananas at £2.55 a kg

3. 5 packets of sweets at £1.19 a packet

4. 4 kg of potatoes at 39 p a kg

5. 3.2 kg of carrots at 45 p a kg

B   1. Tim had a meal.
He paid with a £20 note.
How much change will he get?

2. 13 friends had a meal.
How much will this cost altogether?

3. Lisa had a meal.
She only had 85 p left after she had paid for it.
How much did she have to start with?

4. A group of people had a meal.
It cost £75.60 altogether.
How many were in the group?

MEALS
~
£8.40
each

C   How much are these?

1. 5 packets of crisps

2. 7 cans of drink

3. 2 packets of crisps and a chocolate bar

4. 6 cans of drink and 4 packets of crisps

5. 4 cans of drink and 2 packets of crisps

Crisps 27p   Cans 29p   Choc bars 50p

Reading the calculator answer

Sometimes the calculator gives us an answer like this.

$$5.2631579$$

Example   Tim wanted to know how many 19 p stamps he could buy for £1. 19 p is £0.19.

He keyed.

| 1 | ÷ | 0 | · | 1 | 9 | = | and got 5.2631579

The 5 means 5 ones.

The part after the decimal point means a bit of one.

So Tim could buy only 5 stamps.

Exercise 7

A   1.   How many 23 p bags of fudge could Tim buy for £1?

2.   How many 27 p packets of crisps could Tim buy for £2?

3.   How many 80 p rides could Tim have for £3?

HILLVIEW FAIR
● All Rides 80p ●

4.   How many 35 p drinks could Tim have for £1.50?

B

BEST DISCO

Entry £4.50
Drinks 20p each

TOP DISCO

Drinks
60p
each

Entry £2.80

1.   How much would it cost Tim to go to each of these discos and have 4 drinks?

2.   Lisa had £5 for entry and drinks.
     How many drinks could Lisa have at Best Disco?

3.   Siana had £5 for entry and drinks.
     How many drinks could Siana have at Top Disco?

Example Mr. Sim wanted to know how many boats he needed to book for 257 people.

He keyed

He got **4.6727273**

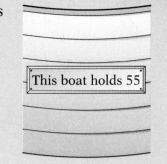

This boat holds 55

The 4 means 4 ones.
The part after the decimal point means a bit of one.
He needs 4 and a bit boats.
He can't book a bit of a boat.
So he needs to book 5 boats.

Exercise 8

A How many of these buses would be needed for

1. 60 people   2. 141 people
3. 227 people   4. 289 people
5. 314 people   6. 582 people?

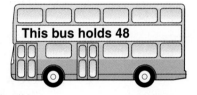

This bus holds 48

B How many times must the lift go up if this number of people are waiting?

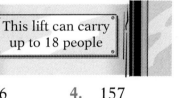

This lift can carry up to 18 people

1. 30   2. 89   3. 126   4. 157
5. 175   6. 211   7. 269

C Sue has a job weeding gardens.
She saves £23 each week.
How many weeks will it take for her to save for these?

1.  £99.50

2.  £129.99

3.  £149.50

Homework/Review 2

A What goes through water but doesn't get wet?

A				A				
‾‾‾‾‾	‾‾‾‾‾	‾‾‾‾‾	‾‾‾‾‾			‾‾‾‾‾	‾‾‾‾‾	
10.12	6.585	10.12	46.8			2.15	21.5	

‾‾‾‾‾　‾‾‾‾‾　‾‾‾‾‾　‾‾‾‾　‾‾‾‾‾
65.85　4.68　97.66　4.6　101.2

Use a copy of this box.
Use a calculator to find the answers to these.

A	$3.7 + 6.42 = 10.12$	F	4.3×5	I	$19 - 14.32$
H	$32.2 \div 7$	Y	7.8×6	T	$157.5 - 56.3$
O	$17.2 \div 8$	L	$8.36 + 57.49$	R	1.317×5
G	$187.3 - 89.64$				

B　Find the cost of 3.4 kg of apples at 95 p a kg.

C　1.　How much does it cost to go
　　　　into the castle and have a tour?

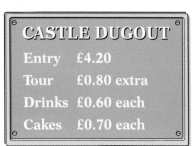

CASTLE DUGOUT
Entry　£4.20
Tour　£0.80 extra
Drinks　£0.60 each
Cakes　£0.70 each

2.　Maria has £6 to go into the castle
　　and buy a drink and a cake.
　　Has she got enough for a tour
　　as well?

3.　Bob paid to go into the castle with a £20 note.
　　How much change will he get?

4.　A group paid £33.60 to get into the castle.
　　How many were in the group?

5.　Mandy had £2.90 left over at the end of the tour.
　　She wanted to buy cakes for her friends.
　　How many could she buy?

6.　One busy day 165 people
　　were waiting for horse
　　and cart rides.

CASTLE
HORSE AND CART RIDES
No more than 14
on the cart please

　　How many rides will need
　　to be given?

◀◀ CHAPTER REVIEW ◀◀

◀◀
Exercise 1
on page 190

A Check the answers to each of these in 2 ways.
If the answer is wrong write down the right answer.
1. 869 – 324 = 572   2. 1288 ÷ 23 = 65

◀◀
Exercise 2
on page 190

B Use a calculator to find the answers to these.
1. 23 × 62   2. 386 – 129   3. 1352 ÷ 52
4. 827 + 271   5. 152 × 61   6. 486 – 137
7. 3942 ÷ 73   8. 1862 + 341   9. 11 869 – 9830
10. 10 971 ÷ 69   11. 183 × 72

◀◀
Exercise 4
on page 192

C

◀──────────── 86 cm ────────────▶

1. Jill bought 26 pieces of this carved wood.
How many centimetres does she have altogether?

2. Sam needed 774 centimetres of this wood.
How many pieces of it will he need?

3. Jon bought 946 cm of the wood.
He only used 796 cm of it.
How much has he got left?

◀◀
Exercise 5
on page 196

D Use your calculator to find the answers to these.
1. 4.6 + 7.9   2. 4.35 + 27.62   3. 4.1 × 9
4. 89.6 – 5.31   5. 31.5 ÷ 5   6. 47.3 × 0.69
7. 419.34 ÷ 5.8   8. 0.634 – 0.231

◀◀
Exercises 6,
7 and 8 on
pages 197,
198 and 199

E 1. Dan bought a camera.
He paid with a £50 note.
How much change did he get?

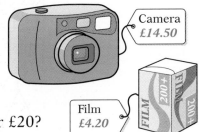

Camera
£14.50

2. He paid £25.20 for some films.
How many did he buy?

3. How many films can Greg buy for £20?

Film
£4.20

4. Greg can take 24 pictures on each film.
He wants to take 224 pictures.
How many films does he need?

Quick Test 5

A Rex makes t-shirts.

He makes patterns for them by reflecting shapes.

1. Use a copy of this.

Reflect these in the mirror line.

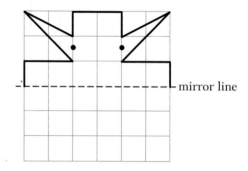

mirror line

mirror line

2. Use a copy of this.

Reflect the shape in one mirror line to make a pattern.

Then reflect the whole pattern in the other mirror line.

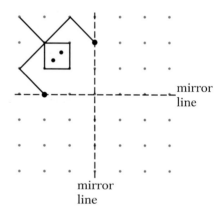

mirror line

mirror line

3. Use a copy of this.

Rex chose this shape.

He made a tiling pattern with it.

Finish Rex's tiling pattern.

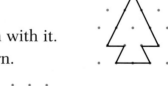

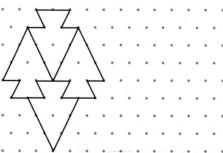

B

	Sales			
	month 1	month 2	month 3	month 4
t-shirt A	1286	3385	5973	71 872
t-shirt B	1179	2276	3654	8964

1. How many t-shirts did Rex sell altogether in month 1?

2. How many of t-shirt A did he sell altogether?

3. How many more of t-shirt A did he sell than t-shirt B?

4. He sold each t-shirt A for £7.
   How much did he get in month 3 for these?

C Use the sales chart in **B** to answer these.

1. Give the number of t-shirt A sold in month 4 to the nearest 10.

2. Give the number of t-shirt B sold in month 4 to the nearest 100.

3. Rex sent a parcel of t-shirts.
   It weighed 16.7 kg.
   Give this to the nearest kg.

D In the first month Rex's t-shirts sold for £24 081.
He wrote to his sister.
What is a sensible amount to go in the gap?
In the first month I sold about £ _____ of t-shirts.

E Rex sent this bill to a shop.

1. Show, without doing a calculation, that it is added wrongly.

2. Calculate the correct amount to pay.

REX T-SHIRTS

T-shirt A   £98.00

T-shirt B   £191.85

To pay   £399.85

F Rex sells his t-shirt B for £12.79.

1. How much would 13 of these cost?

2. Brian has £100 to spend on t-shirts.
   How many of t-shirt B could he buy?

16 Perimeter and Area

Shortest way..

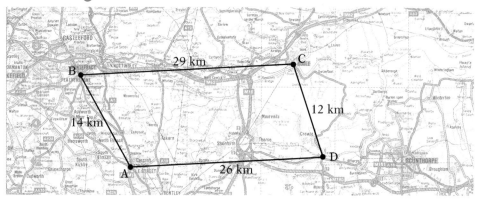

How far is it from A to C if you go through B?

How far is it from A to C if you go through D?

Which is the shortest way?
How far is it from A to B to C to D to A again?

Perimeter

The distance right around the outside of a shape is called the **perimeter**.

An ant walked around the perimeter of this shape. It walked

8 + 12 + 4 + 16 = 40 cm

Perimeter is a length.
It is measured in mm or cm or m or km or inches or feet or miles.

Example   The perimeter of this park is

2 + 3 + 1 + 2 + 3 = 11 km

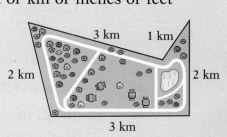

Exercise 1   Find the perimeter of these.

1.
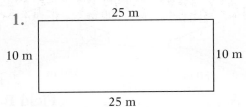

2.
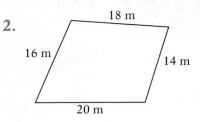

3.
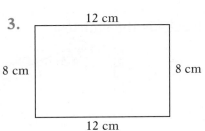

4.
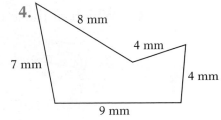

5.
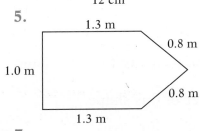

6.
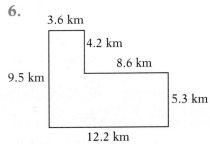

7.
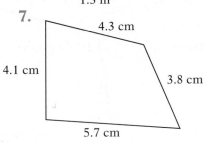

Exercise 2   **A**   **1.** Laura walked right round the edge of this pool. How far did she walk?

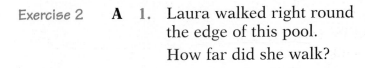

2. Kate ran right round the edge of this park. How far did she run?

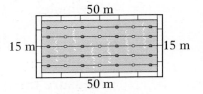

3. A car drove round this track. How far did it go?

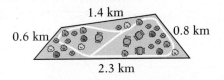

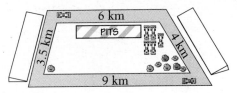

B   Which of these fields has the biggest perimeter?

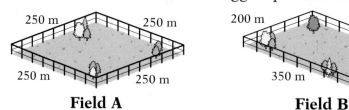

Field A   **Field B**

C   Which of these car tracks is the shortest?

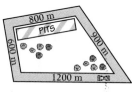   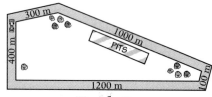

Track A   **Track B**

Sometimes we have to **measure the perimeter**.

Example   Measure the perimeter of this shape.

Measure to the nearest millimetre.

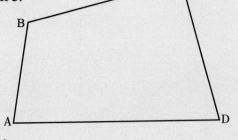

Answer   length of AB = 27 mm

length of BC = 43 mm

length of CD = 38 mm

length of AD = 56 mm

Perimeter = 27 + 43 + 38 + 56

= 164 mm

Exercise 3   Measure the perimeter of these shapes.
Measure to the nearest millimetre.

1.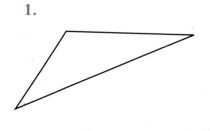

2.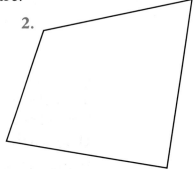

3.

4.

5.

6.

Task

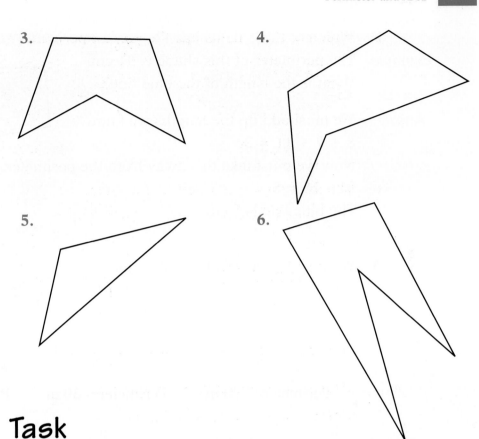

You will need   string
a measuring tape
chalk

- Measure the perimeter of some things in your classroom.
  How could you use the string to help?

- Who has the longest perimeter?

  Put your hands on the concrete outside.

  Spread your hands and legs as far as you can.

  Use chalk to join your hands and legs to make a 4-sided shape.

  Measure the perimeter of your shape.

  Who has the longest perimeter?

Example   The perimeter of this shape is 31 cm.
What is the length of the blue line?

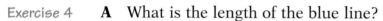

Answer   We must add up the lengths we know.
8 + 7 + 11 = 26
Now we must take this away from the perimeter.
31 − 26 = 5
The blue line is 5 cm.

Exercise 4   **A** What is the length of the blue line?

1.

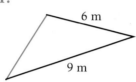

Perimeter = 20 m

2.

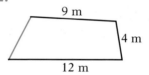

Perimeter = 30 m

3.

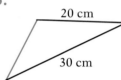

Perimeter = 65 cm

4.

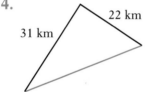

Perimeter = 91 km

5.

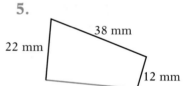

Perimeter = 106 mm

B Tony ran right around
these streets.

He ran 23 km.

What is the length of
Main Street?

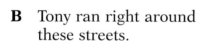

Example   These dots are all 1 cm apart.

If we start at **A** and count each
1 cm length on the perimeter,
we get 10.

The perimeter of this shape is 10 cm.

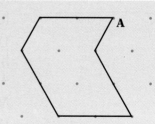

Exercise 5   **A** All the dots in these are 1 cm apart.
Find the perimeter of each shape.

1.   **2.**   **3.**

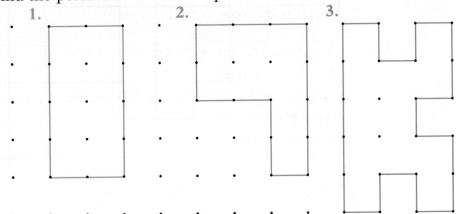

B All the dots in these are 1 cm apart.
Find the perimeter of each shape.

1.   **2.**   **3.**

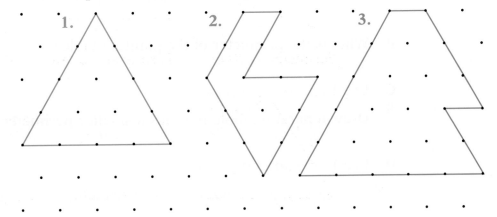

C Use triangle dotty paper
for this question.
Alun drew this shape on
triangle dotty paper.
The dots are 1 cm apart.

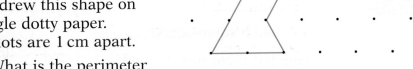

1. What is the perimeter
of Alun's shape?

2. Draw a shape which
has a smaller perimeter
than Alun's.

3. Draw a shape which has
a bigger perimeter
than Alun's.

Exercise 6

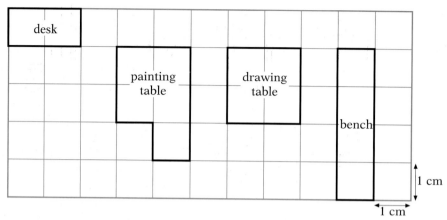

Jan drew this plan of her art room.

A What is the perimeter of these on her plan?

   1. desk   **2.** drawing table   **3.** bench

B What is the perimeter of the painting table?

C Use 1 cm squared paper.

   Draw a painting table that has a smaller perimeter than Jan's.

D Use 1 cm squared paper.

   Draw a bench that has a bigger perimeter than Jan's.

Investigation

Liz had 5 square tables.

She put them next to each other as shown.

Twelve people could sit at these.

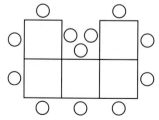

Liz put the tables together in some other ways.

Draw pictures to show how she might have done this.

How many people can sit at the tables in each of your pictures?

Homework/Review 1

What happens when skiers get old?

					$\overset{O}{\rule{1em}{0.4pt}}$
$\overline{\rule{1.5em}{0pt}}$	$\overline{\rule{1.5em}{0pt}}$	$\overline{\rule{1.5em}{0pt}}$	$\overline{\rule{1.5em}{0pt}}$	$\overline{\rule{1.5em}{0pt}}$	
42.9	83	60	28	106	25

	$\overset{O}{\rule{1em}{0.4pt}}$						
$\overline{\rule{1.5em}{0pt}}$		$\overline{\rule{1.5em}{0pt}}$	$\overline{\rule{1.5em}{0pt}}$	$\overline{\rule{1.5em}{0pt}}$	$\overline{\rule{1.5em}{0pt}}$	$\overline{\rule{1.5em}{0pt}}$	$\overline{\rule{1.5em}{0pt}}$
92	25	52	16	83	14.2	22	22

Use a copy of this box.
Find the perimeter of these.

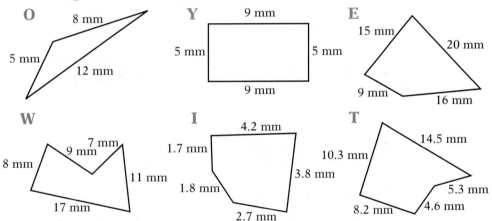

Measure the perimeter of these. The answer is to the nearest mm.

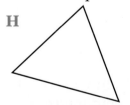

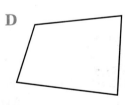

Find the perimeter of these.
All the dots in these are 1 cm apart.

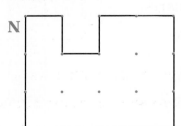

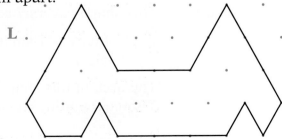

Area

The amount of space covered
by a shape is called its **area**.

These tiles cover 5 squares.

Exercise 7   **A**   How many squares do these tiles cover?

1. 2. 3.

4. 5. 6.

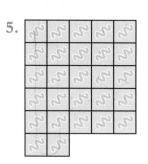

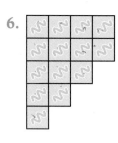

B   How many tiles are needed to finish each of these areas?

1. 2. 3.

This square is 1 cm long and 1 cm wide.
We say this area is one square centimetre.
Sometimes this is written as 1 cm².

Example   This shape covers 7 squares.

Each square is 1 square
centimetre.

The area of this shape is
7 square centimetres or 7 cm².

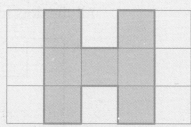

Exercise 8   **A**   What is the area of these shapes?

Each square is 1 cm².

The answer to **1** is 6 cm².

B   Write down the perimeter of each of the shapes in **A**.

C   Use a copy of this.

Marg drew this shape on
1 cm squared paper.

1.   What is the area of
Marg's shape?

2.   Draw a shape which
has a smaller area
than Marg's.

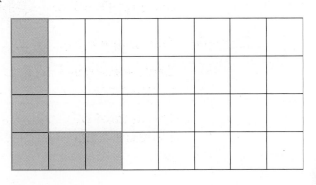

Exercise 9   Nesta is planning to make her own gift paper.
She drew these shapes.
What is the area of each?
The dots are 1 cm apart.

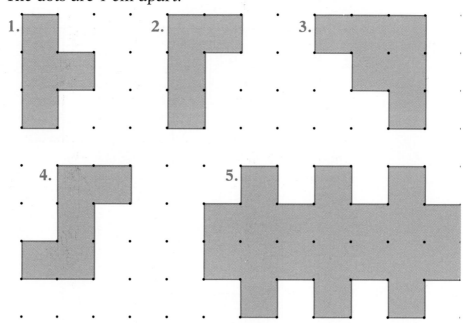

Example   Two half squares make a
whole square.
The area of this shape is
4 squares or 4 cm².

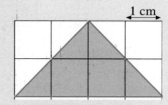

Exercise 10   Use a copy of this.
Count squares to find
the area of these shapes.

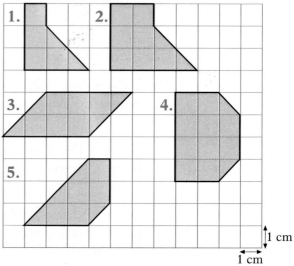

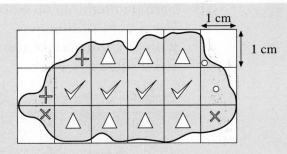

Sometimes we have to
estimate an area.

Each whole square is marked with a ✓.
The ┿ and ┿ make about a whole square.
The ○ and ○ make about a whole square.
The ✕ and ✕ make about a whole square.
The squares marked with a △ are all a bit less than a whole
square. Together we estimate they make about 6 squares.
Counting all of these we get 13 squares.
The area is about 13 cm².

Exercise 11   **A**   Jake drew these shapes on felt.
Use a copy of this.
Count squares to estimate the area of these.

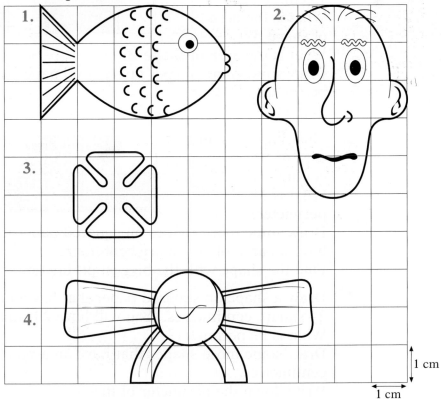

B   Sam painted this on a wall.
Use a copy of this.
Estimate the area of the **1.** dog   **2.** cat   **3.** mouse.
Each square is 1 m².

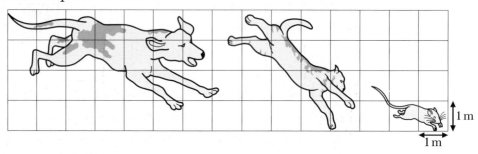

Investigation

You will need   some 1 cm squared paper

1.   The perimeter of
shape A is 12 cm.
The perimeter of
shape B is also
12 cm.
What is the area
of shape A?
of shape A?
What is the area of shape B?
Draw some more shapes on squared paper which have a
perimeter of 12 cm.
Find the shape with the biggest area.

2.   This shape has an
area of 10 square
centimetres.
What is its
perimeter?

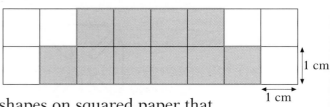

Draw some more shapes on squared paper that
have an area of 10 square centimetres.
Find the shape with the biggest perimeter.

3.   Draw a shape on squared paper that has an area of
24 square centimetres. (You will have 24 squares shaded.)
What is its perimeter?
Draw some more shapes that have an area of 24 square
centimetres.
Write down the perimeter of these.

Homework/Review 2

A **What is the quickest way to make oil boil?**

$$\overline{} \quad \overline{} \quad \overline{} \qquad \overline{} \quad \overline{} \quad \overset{E}{\overline{}}$$

7 cm²   4 cm²   4 cm²   3 cm²   12 cm²   6 cm²

$$\overline{} \quad \overset{E}{\overline{}} \quad \overline{} \quad \overline{} \quad \overset{E}{\overline{}} \quad \overline{} \qquad \overline{}$$

5 cm²   6 cm²   3 cm²   3 cm²   6 cm²   2 cm²   15 cm²

Use a copy of this. What is the area of these?

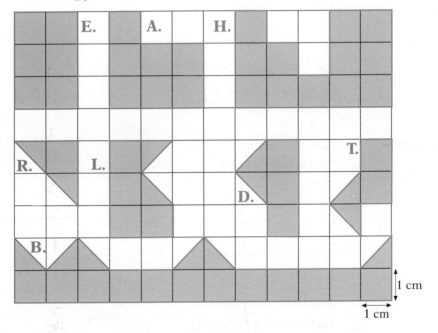

1 cm

1 cm

B Meg painted this on a sign. Estimate its area by counting squares.

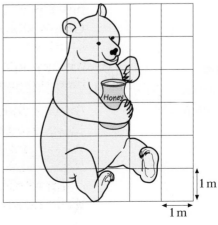

1 m

1 m

◄◄ CHAPTER REVIEW ◄◄

◄◄

Exercise 1
on page 205

A Find the perimeter of these.

1.
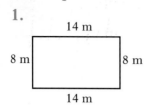

2.
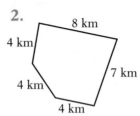

3.
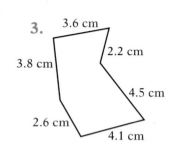

◄◄

Exercise 3
on page 206

B Measure the perimeter of these shapes.
Measure to the nearest mm.

1.
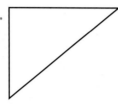

2.
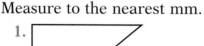

◄◄

Exercise 4
on page 208

C Jo's pool has a perimeter
of 50 m.

What is the length of the
side with the ladder?

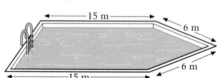

◄◄

Exercise 5
on page 209

D Use a copy of this.
The dots are 1 cm apart.
Greg drew this shape.

1. Find the perimeter.
2. Draw a shape which
   has a perimeter less than
   Greg's shape.

◄◄

Exercise 7
on page 212

E How many squares do these stamps cover?

1.

2.

◀◀
Exercise 8
on page 213

F   What is the area of these shapes? Each square is 1 cm².

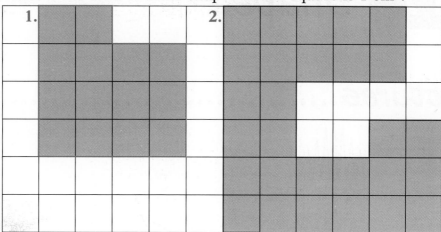

◀◀
Exercise 9
on page 214

G   Rick drew this HB for
Happy Birthday on a card.
The dots are 1 cm apart.
What is the area of
Rick's shape?

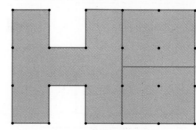

◀◀
Exercises 10
and 11 on
pages 214
and 215

H   Use a copy of this.
Tracy drew this picture on 1 cm squared paper.
1.   Count squares to find the area of the rock.
2.   Estimate the area of the mermaid.

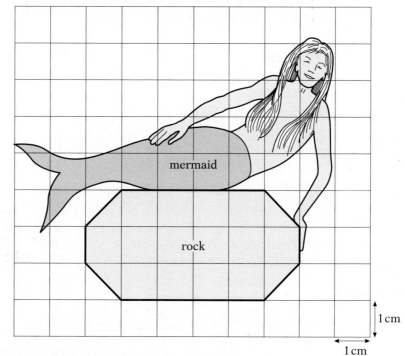

mermaid

rock

1 cm

1 cm

Pictures..

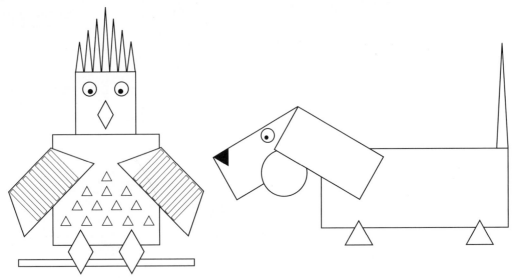

Jake made these shape pictures.
Make a shape picture of your own.
Name all the shapes you have used.

Drawing circles

The distance from the middle
to the outside of the circle is
called the **radius**.

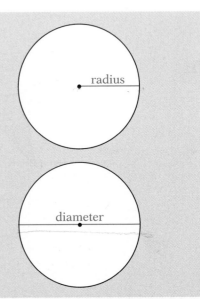

The distance right across the
circle, through the centre,
is the **diameter**.

Exercise 1

A Which line on each of these is the radius?

1. 2. 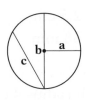 3. 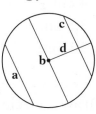 4.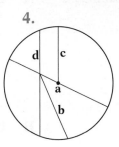

B Which line on each of the circles in **A** is the diameter?

C Measure the diameter of these.

1. 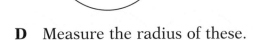 2. 3. 4.

D Measure the radius of these.

1. 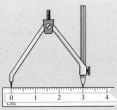 2. 3. 4.

We use a **compass** to draw a circle.
To draw a circle of radius 3 cm
follow these steps.

1. Open the compass to 3 cm.

2. Keep the compass point
   in one place.
   Draw a circle with
   the pencil.

How could you draw a very
big circle, like the landing
pad for a helicopter?

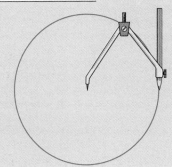

Exercise 2 **A** Draw a circle with this radius.

1. 4 cm   2. 2 cm   3. 5 cm   4. 4.5 cm

5. 3.5 cm   6. 2.5 cm   7. 6 cm   8. 24 mm

9. 30 mm   10. 38 mm

B 1. Draw a circle with radius 4 cm.

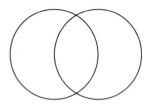

2. Put your compass point anywhere on the outside of this circle. Draw another circle with radius 4 cm.

3. Colour your circles.

C 1. Draw 4 circles of radius 2 cm. Make the circles touch each other.

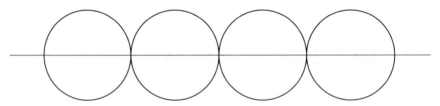

2. Draw 3 more circles of radius 2 cm. Make the centre of these where 2 of the other circles touch.

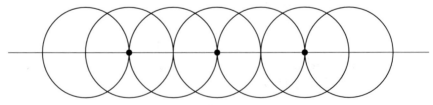

3. Colour these circles to make a pattern. Two examples are shown.

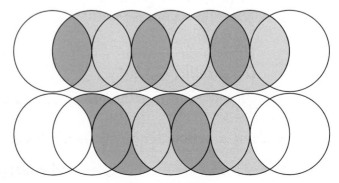

D 1. Draw 4 circles with the same centre but a different radius. You could put lines on them.

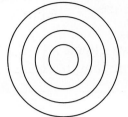  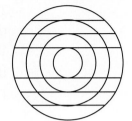

2. Colour your circles.

E 1. Draw half of a circle of radius 3 cm.

2. Draw lots of smaller circles of radius 1.5 cm as shown.

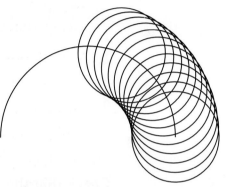

F Draw your own circle pattern.

Drawing squares and rectangles

Task 1

You will need   a piece of paper
a ruler

A Make a set square the same way as you did on **page 89** of **Chapter 7**.

B To draw a rectangle 5 cm by 2 cm follow these steps.

1. Draw a line 5 cm long.

2. Put your set square on one end of the line.

3. Draw a line along the edge of the set square that is 2 cm long.

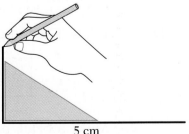

5 cm

4. Finish drawing the rectangle using the set square and ruler.

C Draw some more rectangles and squares this way.

The blue lines are called **diagonals**.
The diagonals of a rectangle are
the same length.
When we draw a rectangle we check
that the diagonals are the same length.

Exercise 3   **A**   Use your set square and ruler to draw these.
Check that the diagonals are the same length.
1.   a square with sides 2 cm
2.   a rectangle with sides 2.5 cm and 4 cm
3.   a rectangle with sides 4 cm and 1.5 cm
4.   a 4 cm by 3 cm rectangle

B   Use your set square and ruler to draw rectangles with
these sides.
Check that the diagonals are the same length.
1.   4 cm by 2 cm   2.   3 cm by 2.5 cm
3.   3.5 cm by 1.5 cm   4.   20 mm by 35 mm
5.   44 mm by 30 mm   6.   38 mm by 28 mm
7.   46 mm by 23 mm   8.   36 mm by 22 mm
9.   17 mm by 28 mm

C   Use your set square and ruler to draw squares with these sides.
Check that the diagonals are the same length.
1.   3 cm   2.   2 cm   3.   4 cm
4.   2.5 cm   5.   3.5 cm   6.   4.5 cm
7.   24 mm   8.   32 mm

D   1.   Draw 3 rectangles, 1 cm by 2 cm, next to each other.

2.   Make a brick pattern
by drawing more
rectangles.

Drawing triangles

We can use a compass and a ruler to **draw a triangle**.

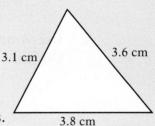

To draw this triangle, follow these steps.

1. Draw a line 3.8 cm long.

2. Open the compass out to 3.1 cm.

   Put the compass point on one end of the line, where the blue dot is.

   Draw a part of a circle.

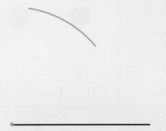

3. Open the compass out to 3.6 cm.

   Put the compass point on the other end of the line.

   Draw a part of a circle.
   Make it cross the other part.

4. Draw the sides.

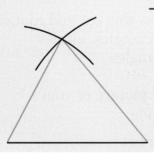

Exercise 4   **A** Use a compass and ruler to draw these.

1.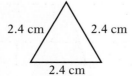

2.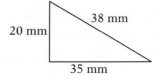

3.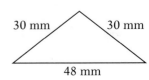

B Use a compass and ruler to draw triangles with these sides.
1. 5 cm, 5.8 cm, 5.5 cm   2. 5 cm, 5 cm, 6 cm
3. 8 cm, 7.5 cm, 6 cm   4. 5.5 cm, 3 cm, 3.8 cm
5. 6 cm, 4 cm, 3.5 cm

C Use your set square, ruler and compass to draw these.
On your drawing, measure the distance shown by the blue line.

1.

2.

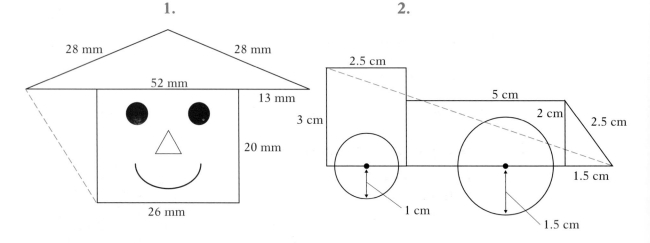

Task 2

You will need   a compass, a ruler and a set square

Jon drew this cat and mouse
with rectangles, circles
and triangles.

Make a picture of your
own using

squares

rectangles

triangles

circles.

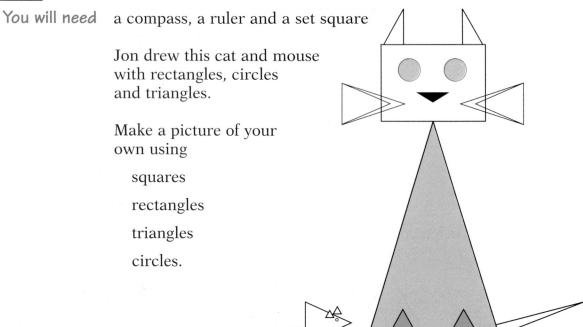

Homework/Review 1

A 1. Which line on this is the radius?

2. Which line is the diameter?

3. Measure the radius.

4. Measure the diameter.

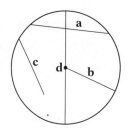

B Draw a circle with this radius.

1. 2 cm
2. 32 mm
3. 18 mm

C 1. Draw a circle of radius 3 cm.

2. Put a mark on the outside of the circle.

Use this as the centre to draw another circle of radius 3 cm.

3. Put a mark at one place where this circle crosses the first circle.

Use this as the centre to draw another circle of radius 3 cm.

4. Draw more circles of radius 3 cm to make the diagram shown.

D Use a set square, compass and ruler to draw this.
On your drawing measure the blue line.

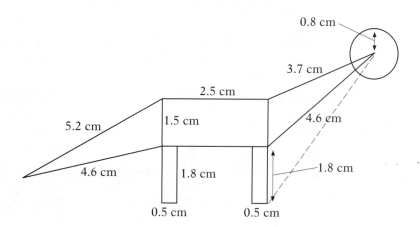

Drawing shapes on grids

We can draw shapes on grids.

Examples

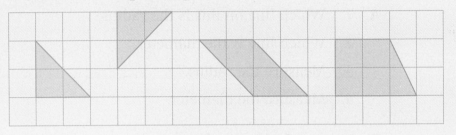

Exercise 5

You will need some squared paper.

1. Tim drew this triangle on squared paper.

   Draw 3 different triangles on your squared paper.

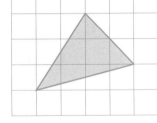

2. Pam drew this shape with 4 sides on squared paper.

   Draw 5 different shapes each with 4 sides on your squared paper.

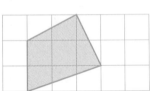

3. Rishi drew the same shape in 2 different positions on the grid.

   Draw Rishi's shape in 2 other different positions on your paper.

   Shade some squares to make a different 6-sided shape.

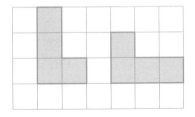

4. Draw each of these shapes in 3 different positions on your grid.

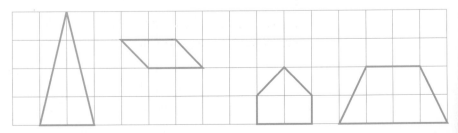

Exercise 6   You will need some triangle grid paper.

A Pete uses a triangle grid to draw shapes.
He shades 3 triangles to make a 4-sided shape.

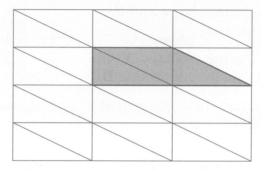

1. Shade 3 triangles on your grid paper to make a different 4-sided shape.

2. Shade 4 triangles on your grid paper to make another different 4-sided shape.

B Make as many different shapes as you can by shading 2 triangles.

C Make as many different shapes as you can by shading 4 triangles.

D Make a big triangle by shading 9 small triangles.

Exercise 7   You will need some triangle dotty paper.

1. Jane drew this 4-sided shape.
Draw 5 different 4-sided shapes on your dotty paper.

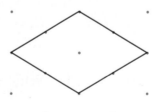

2. Bill drew this 5-sided shape.
Draw 3 more different 5-sided shapes on your dotty paper.

Congruent shapes

Shape **A** and shape **B** are the same shape and the same size.

A tracing of shape **A** will fit exactly over shape **B**.

We call these **congruent** shapes.

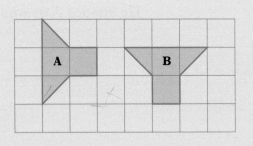

Example   Which shapes are congruent to the blue shape?

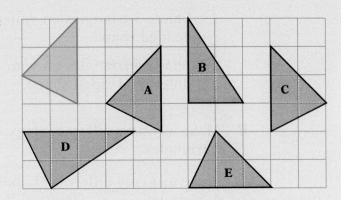

Answer   A tracing of the blue shape will fit exactly on top of shape **A** and shape **C** and shape **E**.

Shape **A**, shape **C** and shape **E** are congruent to the blue shape.

Exercise 8   1.   Which shape is congruent to the blue shape?

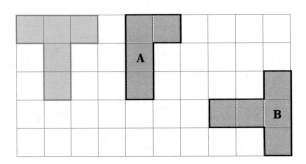

2. Which shapes are congruent to the blue shape?

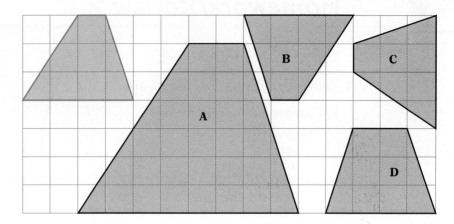

3. Which shapes are congruent to the blue shape?

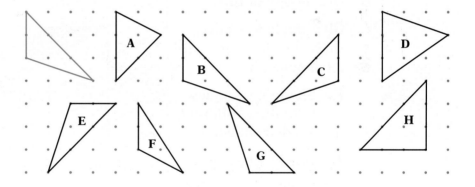

4. Which of these shapes are congruent?

Use tracing paper to check.

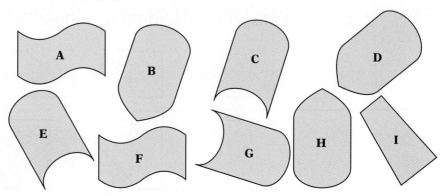

Homework/Review 2

A Use a copy of this.

Becky drew this 5-sided shape.

1. Draw the same shape in a different position on the grid.

2. Draw another 5-sided shape on the grid.

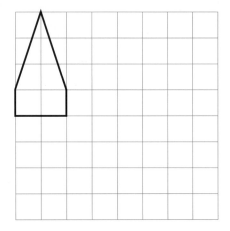

B Use a copy of this.

Glyn made a 4-sided shape by shading 2 triangles.

1. Shade 2 triangles to make a different 4-sided shape.

2. Shade 3 triangles to make a 4-sided shape.

3. Shade 4 triangles to make a 4-sided shape.

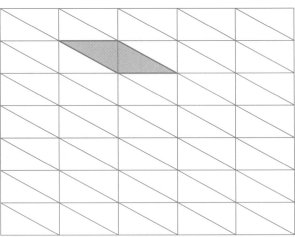

C Which shapes are congruent to the blue shape?

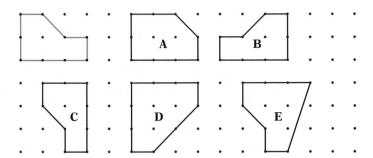

Task 3

You will need some squared paper with squares about this size

1. Draw 12 congruent shapes like this.

    Cut them out.

    Cut out a square with 6 squares along each side.

    Try and fit the 12 shapes onto your square so there are no gaps.

2. Draw 16 congruent shapes like this.

    Cut them out.

    Cut out a square with 8 squares along each side.

    Try and fit the 16 shapes onto your square so there are no gaps.

3. Cut out lots of this shape.
    Try and fit them onto one of your squares.

◄◄ CHAPTER REVIEW ◄◄

◄◄

Exercise 2
on page 222

A 1. Draw a circle with radius 3 cm.

2. Draw another circle with radius 3 cm that just touches the first one.

3. Draw another circle to make this diagram.

4. Colour your circles to make a pattern.

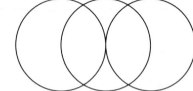

◄◄

Exercises
3 and 4 on
pages 224
and 225

B Use a compass, set square and ruler to draw these.

On your drawing, measure the distance shown by the blue line.

1.

5.6 cm

3.2 cm

6 cm

3.6 cm

4.8 cm

2.

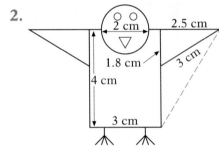

2 cm

2.5 cm

1.8 cm

3 cm

4 cm

3 cm

◄◄

Exercise 5
on page 228

C Use a copy of this.

1. Draw this shape in 3 different positions.

2. Shade some squares to make a different 4-sided shape.

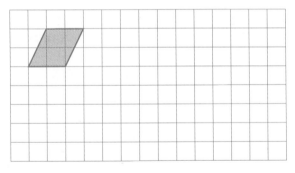

D Which shapes are congruent to the blue shape?

◄◄

Exercise 8
on page 230

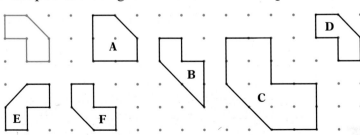

18 Negative Numbers

Hot and cold..

Hot day   **Water turns to ice**   **Very cold place**

What is the temperature on each of these thermometers?
Which one is below zero?

Write down 3 more temperatures that are below zero.

What temperature is your classroom?

Negative numbers

We can use **negative numbers** for lots of things.

Examples

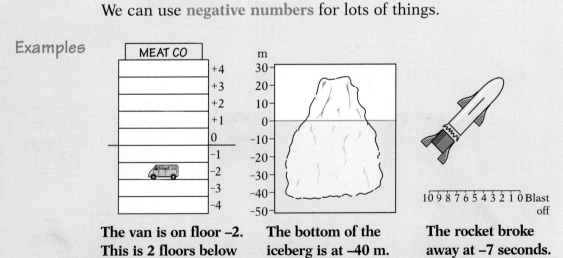

The van is on floor –2.
This is 2 floors below
the ground.

The bottom of the
iceberg is at –40 m.
This is 40 m below
sea level.

The rocket broke
away at –7 seconds.
This is 7 seconds
after blast off.

Exercise 1   **A**   This shows the floors of a building.

What floor are these on?

MEAT CO	
offices	+4
files	+3
orders	+2
cafe	+1
sales	0
cars	-1
trucks	-2
store	-3
freezers	-4

1.   offices   2.   sales

3.   cafe   4.   store

5.   trucks   6.   cars

7.   freezers

B   What is the water level in these rivers?

1. 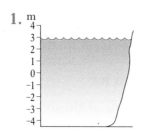   **2.** 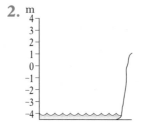   **3.**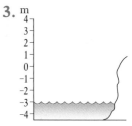

Example   This thermometer reads –7 °C.

Exercise 2   What temperature do these read?

1.   **2.**   **3.**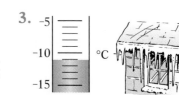

4. 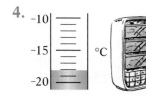   **5.**   **6.**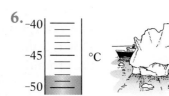

Example

```
      C   S   M   I              E   T   A       H
  |---+---+---+---+---+---+---+---+---+---+---+---+---+---|
              -3              0       2           5
```

Write down the letters which are at these numbers.

−3 3 2 5 1 −3 3 2 −2 −5 −4

What word have you made?

Answer   MATHEMATICS

Exercise 3   **A**

```
   E   N   O   C   I   T   S   N   K   A   H   L   G   J
  |---+---+---+---+---+---+---+---+---+---+---+---+---+---|
          -4              0               4
```

Write down the letters which are at these numbers.

1. 2   −4, 2, −2   −4, 2, 0   4, −5, −5, 1   2, −2   2
   1, −3, −6, 5
   What does the sentence say?

2. −2, 3, −3, −1   −3, −1   0, −5   6, −5, 1, −7
   What does the sentence say?

 B Draw your own number line.

Make up a sentence.

Put the letters in the sentence on your number line.

Write down the sentence using the numbers like **A** above.

Give it to a friend to work out.

Exercise 4

Use a copy of this.

Draw an arrow to show the temperature.

The first one is done.

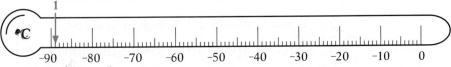

1. −89 °C (coldest temperature ever measured)
2. −27 °C (coldest temperature measured in Britain)
3. −75 °C (dry ice turns to gas)
4. −18 °C (best temperature for a freezer)
5. −13 °C (air temperature on a very cold day)
6. −68 °C (coldest temperature measured in a place where people live)

Using negative numbers

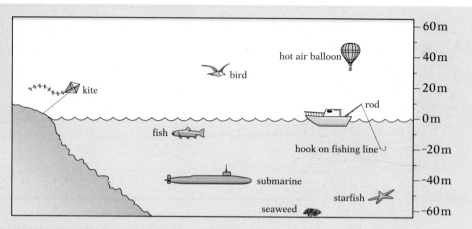

The submarine is at about –40 m.

This means 40 m below sea level.

The submarine is about 20 m below the hook on the fishing line.

Exercise 5   **A**   About what height are the middle of these?

     1. kite   2. hot air balloon   3. seaweed

     4. bird   5. starfish

B

1. What is about 20 m above the kite?

2. What is about 20 m below the bird?

3. What is about 30 m above the hook?

4. What is about 10 m below the hot air balloon?

5. What is about 20 m below the top of the rod?

6. What is about 30 m below the hook?

7. What is about 30 m below the fish?

8. What is about 30 m above the starfish?

9. What is about 20 m above the seaweed?

10. What is about 50 m above the submarine?

11. What is about 40 m above the hook?

12. What is about 80 m below the hot air balloon?

13. What is about 60 m below the top of the rod?

14. What is about 90 m above the seaweed?

Example   A lift started on floor +3 and
went down 5 floors.
Where did it stop?

Answer   It stopped at floor –2.

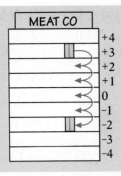

Exercise 6   **A**   What floor does the lift stop at?
1.   It starts on floor +4 and goes down 2 floors.
2.   It starts on floor +3 and goes down 3 floors.
3.   It starts on floor +2 and goes down 3 floors.
4.   It starts on floor +1 and goes down 4 floors.
5.   It starts on floor –1 and goes down 1 floor.
6.   It starts on floor 0 and goes down 3 floors.
7.   It starts on floor –1 and goes down 3 floors.
8.   It starts on floor +2 and goes down 5 floors.

B   What floor does the lift stop at?
1.   It starts at floor +1 and goes up 3 floors.
2.   It starts at floor +2 and goes up 1 floor.
3.   It starts at floor 0 and goes up 4 floors.
4.   It starts at floor –1 and goes up 1 floor.
5.   It starts at floor –2 and goes up 3 floors.
6.   It starts at floor –3 and goes up 1 floor.
7.   It starts at floor –4 and goes up 3 floors.
8.   It starts at floor –4 and goes up 2 floors.

Remember

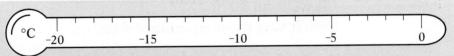

–10 °C is **colder** than –5 °C.
–8 °C is **warmer** than –15 °C.

Exercise 7   What goes in the gap, **warmer** or **colder**?
1.   –5 °C is _____ than   0 °C.
2.   3 °C is _____ than –2 °C.
3.   8 °C is _____ than –3 °C.
4.   –7 °C is _____ than –1 °C.
5.   –6 °C is _____ than –12 °C.
6.   –13 °C is _____ than –5 °C.
7.   –12 °C is _____ than –3 °C.
8.   –27 °C is _____ than 52 °C.

9.   −29 °C is _____ than −36 °C.

10. −42 °C is _____ than −40 °C.

11. −19 °C is _____ than −48 °C.

12. −16 °C is _____ than −30 °C.

13. −52 °C is _____ than −21 °C.

Example

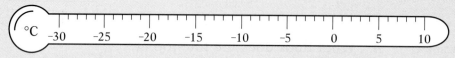

The temperature was −15 °C.
It went up 5 °C.
The new temperature is −10 °C.

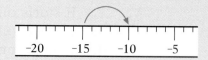

Exercise 8   **A**   Use the thermometer above to help you.

1. The temperature was 0 °C.
   It went up 10 °C.
   What was the temperature then?

2. The temperature was −5 °C.
   It went up 10 °C.
   What was the temperature then?

3. The temperature was −10 °C.
   It went up 20 °C.
   What was the temperature then?

4. The temperature was 10 °C.
   It went down 10 °C.
   What was the temperature then?

5. The temperature was 0 °C.
   It went down 20 °C.
   What was the temperature then?

6. The temperature was −5 °C.
   It went down 10 °C.
   What was the temperature then?

B Use a copy of this table.
Fill it in. Use the thermometer to help.

	Temperature at start	Temperature went up	Temperature after it went up
1.	2 °C	6 °C	8 °C
2.	5 °C	12 °C	
3.	−3 °C	3 °C	
4.	−2 °C	5 °C	
5.	−10 °C	5 °C	
6.	−10 °C	14 °C	
7.	−8 °C	10 °C	
8.	−8 °C	12 °C	
9.	−7 °C	3 °C	
10.	−6 °C	4 °C	
11.	−11 °C	10 °C	
12.	−8 °C	5 °C	
13.	−10 °C	4 °C	
14.	−15 °C	8 °C	
15.	−12 °C	15 °C	
16.	−13 °C	8 °C	

C Use a copy of this table.
Fill it in. Use the thermometer to help.

	Temperature at start	Temperature went down	Temperature after it went down
1.	5 °C	7 °C	−2 °C
2.	10 °C	8 °C	
3.	15 °C	6 °C	
4.	0 °C	8 °C	
5.	0 °C	9 °C	
6.	5 °C	8 °C	
7.	8 °C	9 °C	
8.	10 °C	12 °C	
9.	−2 °C	2 °C	
10.	−4 °C	3 °C	
11.	−5 °C	4 °C	
12.	−6 °C	6 °C	
13.	−10 °C	3 °C	
14.	−12 °C	4 °C	
15.	−11 °C	6 °C	

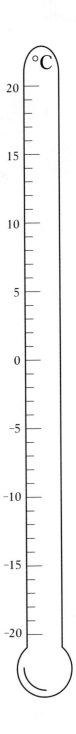

Homework/Review 1

A

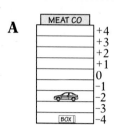 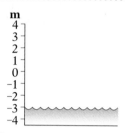 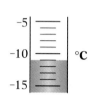

What number goes in the gap?

1. The car is on floor _____ .
2. The box is on floor _____ .
3. The water level in the river is at _____ m.
4. The thermometer is reading _____ °C.

B

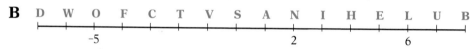

Why is a boxer's hand never larger than 11 inches?

To find the answer write the letters, in order, which are at these numbers.

3, –4   3, –2   –6, 1, 0   –2, –6, 5, 6, –1, 5

3, 2, –3, 4, 5, 0   3, –2   –6, –5, 7, 6, –7   8, 5

1   –4, –5, –5, –2

C

1. What is about 5 m below the dragonfly?
2. What is about 10 m below the bee?
3. What is about 15 m above the fish?
4. What is about 25 m above the diver?
5. What is about 25 m below the bee?

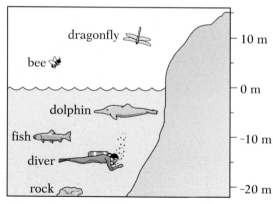

D

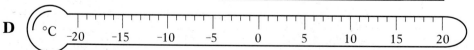

The temperature starts at –5 °C.
What would it be if

1. it went up 5 °C
2. it went down 8 °C
3. it went up 7 °C
4. it went down 6 °C
5. it went up 3 °C?

Game for 2 players: GOLD

You will need   a cube with the numbers 1, 2, 3 and –1, –2, –3 on it
the board below
a counter for each player

To play
- Put the counters on the START square.
- Toss the cube.
- If you toss a 1, 2 or 3 move **towards the gold**.
- If you toss a –1, –2 or –3 move **towards the trap door**.

Examples   If you toss –2, move 2 squares towards the trap door.
If you toss 3, move 3 squares towards the gold.

- If a player reaches GOLD this player is the winner.
- If a player reaches the TRAP DOOR, the other player is the winner.

Putting negative numbers in order

| $-7°C$ | $-4°C$ | $-9°C$ | $13°C$ |

–9 °C is the coldest temperature.
13 °C is the warmest temperature.

Exercise 9   **A** | $-5°C$ | $1°C$ | $0°C$ | $-10°C$ | $6°C$ |

      1.   Which of these temperatures is the coldest?
      2.   Which is the warmest?

B   Which temperature in each of the following is the warmest?

1.	–3 °C,	–8 °C,	5 °C,	12 °C	
2.	–16 °C,	14 °C,	0 °C,	–5 °C	
3.	–12 °C,	5 °C,	–3 °C,	–1 °C	
4.	–36 °C,	–28 °C,	14 °C,	29 °C	
5.	–6 °C,	–3 °C,	–8 °C,	–1 °C	
6.	–16 °C,	–12 °C,	–20 °C,	–3 °C	
7.	–19 °C,	–13 °C,	–23 °C,	–17 °C,	–16 °C
8.	–12 °C,	–16 °C,	–39 °C,	–28 °C,	0 °C
9.	–11 °C,	–4 °C,	–21 °C,	–29 °C,	–52 °C
10.	–31 °C,	–16 °C,	–27 °C,	–33 °C,	–42 °C
11.	–5 °C,	0 °C,	–1 °C,	–2 °C,	–3 °C, –15 °C

C   Which temperature in each of the lists in **B** is the coldest?

Example | $-6°C$ | $-13°C$ | $-23°C$ | $1°C$ | $-5°C$ |

These temperatures in order from coldest to warmest are
–23 °C,   –13 °C,   –6 °C,   –5 °C,   1 °C

Exercise 10   **A**   Put these in order from coldest to warmest.

1.	–1 °C,	5 °C,	0 °C,	–3 °C,	1 °C
2.	–10 °C,	4 °C,	–2 °C,	5 °C,	0 °C
3.	–6 °C,	2 °C,	5 °C,	0 °C,	–8 °C
4.	–9 °C,	0 °C,	–16 °C,	8 °C,	–3 °C
5.	4 °C,	–6 °C,	3 °C,	–1 °C,	–10 °C
6.	20 °C,	–20 °C,	–10 °C,	–5 °C,	–13 °C
7.	16 °C,	–1 °C,	–7 °C,	–8 °C,	–13 °C
8.	–5 °C,	–11 °C,	–1 °C,	6 °C,	–15 °C
9.	–5 °C,	–25 °C,	0 °C,	16 °C,	–3 °C
10.	–17 °C,	2 °C,	–3 °C,	–5 °C,	–13 °C

B These were the overnight temperatures for some cities.

New York –6 °C   Warsaw   –2 °C   Moscow –8 °C
Kiev   –3 °C   Montreal –15 °C

1. Which city had the coldest night?
2. Which city had the warmest night?
3. Put the temperatures in order. Put the coldest first.

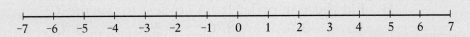

-7   -6   -5   -4   -3   -2   -1   0   1   2   3   4   5   6   7

As we move ⟶ along the number line the numbers get bigger.

As we move ⟵ along the number line the numbers get smaller.

Examples   7 is bigger than –2.

–4 is smaller than –1.

Exercise 11   **A** Which of these numbers is bigger?

1. 0 or 4   2. –2 or 0   3. –1 or 0   4. –3 or 5
5. –7 or –8   6. –5 or –1   7. –12 or –9   8. –6 or –11
9. –5 or –10   10. –12 or 2   11. –15 or –19   12. –24 or –19
13. –31 or –28

B Which of these numbers is smaller?

1. –3 or 0   2. –7 or 2   3. –6 or –11
4. –1 or –5   5. –13 or –17   6. –8 or –14
7. –21 or –13   8. 0 or –14   9. 5 or –1
10. 23 or –3   11. –14 or –29   12. –6 or –18
13. –29 or –21

C Put these numbers in order from biggest to smallest.

1. –1, 0, 3, 8, –4   2. –4, 8, –3, 5, 0
3. 0, –2, –12, 10, –7   4. 8, –3, –1, –11, 1
5. –6, 8, –5, –3, 4   6. –1, –6, –3, –2, –9
7. –15, –13, –8, –3, –2   8. –15, –1, –8, –12, –5
9. –11, –8, –1, –15, –13   10. –9, –12, –15, 0, 4
11. –19, –16, –1, –8, –3

Homework/Review 2

A

-2°C	-9°C	-5°C	-7°C	0°C
City A	City B	City C	City D	City E

1. Which city was the coldest?
2. Which city was the warmest?
3. Put the temperatures in order from warmest to coldest.

B Put these in order from coldest to warmest.

1.   –3 °C,   –8 °C,   5 °C,   0 °C
2.   11 °C,   –11 °C,   8 °C,   –8 °C
3.   –10 °C,   1 °C,   0 °C,   –5 °C,   3 °C
4.   –20 °C,   3 °C,   –5 °C,   8 °C,   0 °C
5.   –16 °C,   0 °C,   8 °C,   –10 °C,   –1 °C

C Put these in order from biggest to smallest.

1. 5, 10, –1, 0, –3, 2
2. 0, –3, –5, 10, –1
3. 8, –3, 0, –6, –11
4. –7, –1, –8, –11, –4
5. –14, –9, –8, –12, –6
6. –1, –7, 8, –5, –2

Puzzles

1. I am a negative number.
   I am bigger than –5.
   I am smaller than –3.
   What number am I?

2.

–5	–3	–2	–1	0
–3	–4	–1	0	1
–2	–3	0	–1	2
–1	0	3	1	4
0	1	4	5	6

Start in the blue square.

Finish in the grey square.

You may move or or or

or but **not** or or

You can only move to a square
that has a bigger number in it.
How many paths can you find?

| More than 15 – Excellent |
| 10 to 15 – Very Good |
| 7 to 9 – Good |

◄◄ CHAPTER REVIEW ◄◄

◄◄
Exercises 1
and 2 on
page 236

A

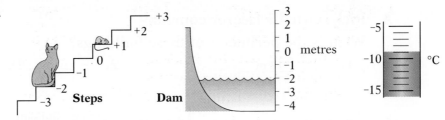

What number goes in the gap?
1. The mouse is on step _____ .
2. The cat is on step _____ .
3. The water level in the dam is _____ metres.
4. The temperature on the thermometer is _____ °C.

◄◄
Exercise 4
on page 237

B Use a copy of this.

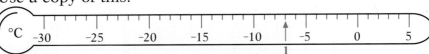

Draw an arrow to show these temperatures.
The first one is done.
1. –7 °C   2. –12 °C   3. 3 °C   4. –18 °C   5. –26 °C

◄◄
Exercise 8
on page 240

C Use the thermometer in **B** to help you.
1. The temperature is 5 °C.
   It goes down 10 °C .
   What is the temperature now?

2. The temperature is –3 °C.
   It goes up 8 °C.
   What is the temperature now?

3. The temperature is –8 °C.
   It goes down 4 °C.
   What is the temperature now?

◄◄
Exercise 10
on page 244

D

Write these in order, warmest first.

◄◄
Exercise 11
on page 245

E Put these in order from smallest to biggest.
1. –3, 0, –2, 4, 8   2. 5, –2, 7, 0, –6
3. –4, –1, 5, 9, –3   4. –2, –5, –1, –6, –9
5. –11, –1, –7, –14, –20

Quick Test 6

A Rick started a freezer company.
What is the perimeter of these buildings?

1.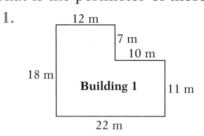

   12 m
   7 m
   10 m
   18 m
   Building 1
   11 m
   22 m

2.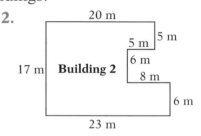

   20 m
   5 m | 5 m
   6 m
   17 m | **Building 2**
   8 m
   6 m
   23 m

B Rick drew the plans for the garages on squared paper.
Each square is 1 m².
What is the area of each of these?

1.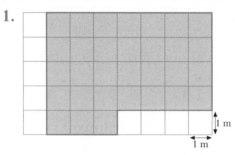

   1 m
   1 m

2.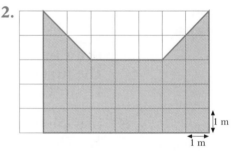

   1 m
   1 m

C An artist drew this picture
for the wall of one building.
Each square is to be 1 m².
Use a copy of this.
Estimate the area of
the picture.

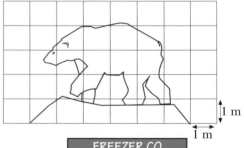

1 m
1 m

D One building had these floors.
What floor does the lift stop at?

1. It starts on floor –2 and goes
   up 4 floors.

2. It starts on floor 2 and goes
   down 4 floors.

3. It starts on floor –1 and goes
   down 2 floors.

FREEZER CO	
	3
	2
	1
	0
	–1
	–2
	–3
	–4

E   Rick drew this 'F' for his company.

Use a compass, set square and ruler to draw this.

On your drawing, measure the length of the blue line.

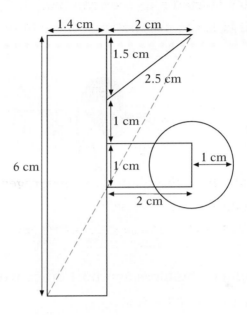

F   Rick drew a different 'F' for his freezer company.

Which ones are congruent to the blue 'F'?

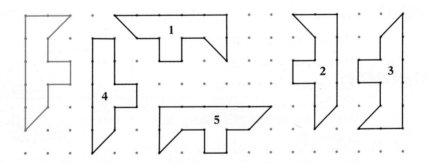

G   Rick took the temperature in each freezer.

Put these in order from coldest to warmest.

–15 °C,   –12 °C,   –5 °C,   –13 °C,   –20 °C,   0 °C,   –18 °C

19 Measures

On the job....................................

Painters, builders and post office workers all use measures.

Write down 3 other jobs.

What needs to be measured in these jobs?

Make a list.

What would you use to measure each with?

Choosing units

Remember . . .

We measure length using **km**, **m**, **cm**, **mm** or **miles**, **feet** and **inches**.

We measure weight using **kg**, **g**, or **pounds**.

We measure how much water something holds using *l*, **m*l*** or **pints**.

km, m, cm, mm, miles, feet, inches, kg, g, pounds, *l*, m*l*, pints are called **units** of measurement.

Exercise 1

| kg   g   *l*   ml   km   m   cm |

What units would be on each of these?
Choose from the box.

1.   2.   3.   4.

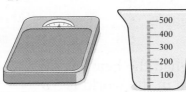

When we measure very heavy things we use **tonnes**.
An elephant could weigh about 4 tonnes.
A lorry could weigh about 6 tonnes.

Exercise 2

Which of these would we weigh in tonnes?

| a van | a cat | a petrol tanker | a tiger |
| a tree | a baby | a school bag | a train |

Exercise 3   **A**   Which unit would these
be measured in?
Choose from the box.

| km   m   cm   mm |

1. how wide a netball court is
2. how long a motorway is
3. how wide a stamp is
4. how high a building is
5. how long your finger is
6. how thick a coin is
7. how long the Thames River is
8. how far it is to Paris
9. how long an ant is

B   Which unit would these
be weighed in?
Choose from the box.

| tonne   kg   g |

1. a dog   2. a ship   3. a pencil
4. a small cake   5. a bag of sweets   6. an orange
7. a lorry full of stones

C Which unit would you use to measure how much water these could hold?

Choose from the box. | l ml |

1. a bucket   2. a cup   3. a washing machine
4. a spoon   5. a pot   6. a coke bottle

Exercise 4   What unit goes in the gap?

Choose from the box. | km m cm mm tonnes kg g |

1. The man who weighed the heaviest ever weighed 635 _____ .
2. The shortest person in the world is 57 _____ tall.
3. The tallest man ever was 272 _____ tall.
4. The tallest living woman is 2.32 _____ tall.
5. The heaviest baby ever born weighed 10 _____ .

Estimating

Remember . . .

An **estimate** is a good guess.

Task 1

You will need a tape measure
a measuring jug
a set of scales

Work with a friend.

1.

	Estimate	Real length
distance around head		
arm length		
hand span		
distance around wrist		
distance from knee to floor		
length of shoe		

Use a copy of this table.
Estimate each of the things in the table.
Get your friend to check your estimates.

2.

Fill some containers with water.
Estimate how much water is in each.
Check using a measuring jug.
Use a copy of this table and fill it in.

Container	Estimate	Real amount

3.

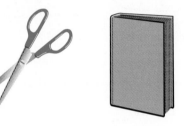 

Choose 5 objects.
Estimate how much each weighs.
Check using some scales.
Use a copy of this table and fill it in.

Objects	Estimate	Real weight

Exercise 5

What number goes in the gap? | 1   2   20   180   250 |
Choose from the box.

1. A desk could be about _____ metre high.
2. A book could be about _____ mm wide.
3. A banana could be about _____ cm long.
4. A van could weigh about _____ tonnes.
5. A cup could hold about _____ m*l*.

Sometimes we need to **estimate numbers** of things.

Example   How many dots do you think
there are?

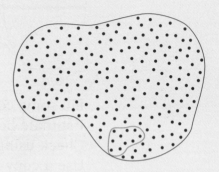

Answer   A ring is drawn around 10 dots.
About how many rings this size
are there?
There are about 20.
$10 \times 20 = 200$
There are about 200 dots.

Exercise 6   Estimate how many dots there are in these.

1.

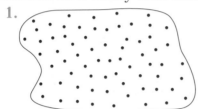

2.

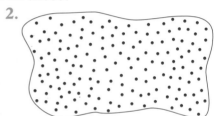

Task 2

You will need   a jar full of peas or beans

Estimate how many peas are in the jar.
When everyone has had a guess, count them.

Example   The tree in this picture is 5 m high.
About how high are the other things?

Answer   The building is about the same height as the tree.
It is about 5 m high.

We can divide the picture into metres in our mind.
The swing is about 2 m high.
The car is about $1\frac{1}{2}$ m high.

Exercise 7   This car is 4 m long.

About how long are these?

1. bus

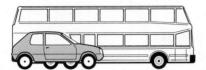

2. car trailer

3. train

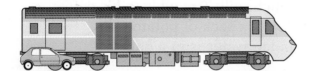

4. bike

Sometimes we measure to the **nearest centimetre** or the **nearest millimetre**.

Measuring to the nearest millimetre is the same as measuring to the nearest 0.1 cm.

Example

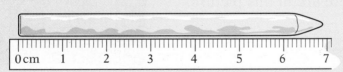

This crayon is 6.9 cm to the nearest 0.1 cm.

Task 3

....

You will need   a ruler

Measure these things to the nearest 0.1 cm.

a desk   a book   a pen   a pencil

Homework/Review 1

A

| km | m | cm | mm | tonne | kg | g | *l* | m*l* |

Which unit would these be measured in?
Choose from the box.

1. how long a building is
2. how heavy a bird is
3. how heavy a cup is
4. how thick a ruler is
5. how wide a pill is
6. how far it is to New York from London
7. how much milk Tim adds to his coffee
8. how heavy a sack of potatoes is
9. how much water is in a bath

B What number goes in the gap?
Choose from the box.

| 3 | 30 | 300 | 3000 |

1. A book could be about _____ centimetres long.
2. A big jug could hold about _____ pints of milk.
3. A bookcase could be about _____ metres long.

C Estimate how many people there are in this picture.

D

The tree in this picture is 10 m tall.
About how tall are these?

1. the pylon   2. the church   3. the bus   4. the house

Reading scales

Remember   Sometimes not every number is shown on a scale.
We must work out what the dashes stand for.

Example

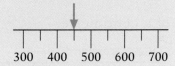

To go from 400 to 500 we must
count in fifties.
Each mark on this scale is 50.
The arrow is at 450.

Example

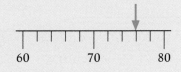

To go from 70 to 80 we must count
in twos.
Each mark on the scale is 2.
The pointer is at 76.

Example

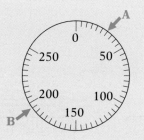

To go from 0 to 50 we must count
in fives.
Each mark on the scale is 5.
A is at 30.
B is at 195.

Exercise 8   **What are these arrows pointing to?**

1.

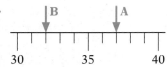

2.

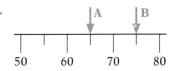

3.

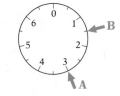

4.

5.

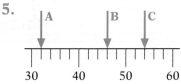

6.

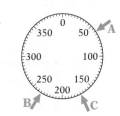

Decimals in measurement

This scale is split up into 10.

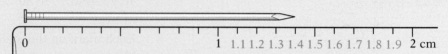

0   1 cm

Each mark is one tenth of a centimetre.

One tenth is 0.1.

The tack is 0.6 cm long.

0   0.1 0.2 0.3 0.4 0.5 0.6 0.7 0.8 0.9   1 cm

Example

0   1   1.1 1.2 1.3 1.4 1.5 1.6 1.7 1.8 1.9   2 cm

This nail is 1.4 cm long.

Exercise 9   How long are these?

1.

2.

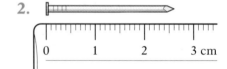

0   1   2 cm

0   1   2   3 cm

3.

4.

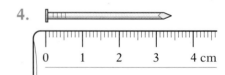

0   1   2   3   4 cm

0   1   2   3   4 cm

5.

6.

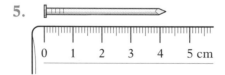

0   1   2   3   4   5 cm

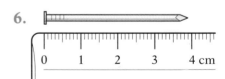

0   1   2   3   4 cm

7.

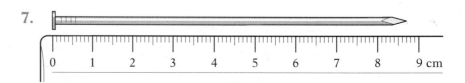

0   1   2   3   4   5   6   7   8   9 cm

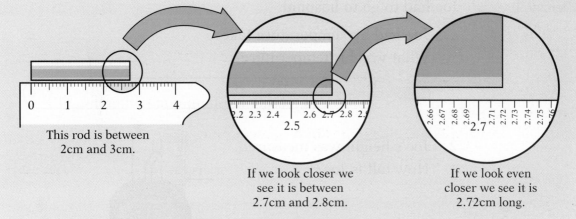

This rod is between
2cm and 3cm.

If we look closer we
see it is between
2.7cm and 2.8cm.

If we look even
closer we see it is
2.72cm long.

Each mark on the last scale is one hundredth of a centimetre.
One hundredth is 0.01.

Example

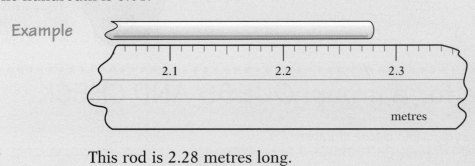

This rod is 2.28 metres long.

Exercise 10   What do these arrows read?

1.

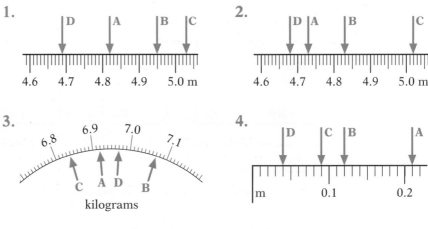

2.

3.

4.

5.

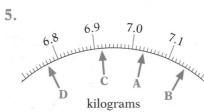

Exercise 11   Joe had to go to hospital.

1. Joe had his temperature taken.
    What was his temperature?

2. Joe's height was measured.
    How tall is Joe?

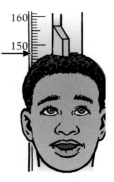

Game for a group: GUESS AND CHECK

You will need   some pieces of paper
pencil
ruler

To play   • Each player draws a straight line on a piece of paper.

• Mix up the pieces of paper.

• Choose one piece of paper.

• Each player guesses how long the line is and writes it down in a table like this.

Line	My guess	Real length	Points
1	4.6 cm	5.2 cm	3

• Measure the line.

• The player who guessed closest gets 5 points.
The next closest gets 4 points.
The next closest gets 3 points.
The next closest gets 2 points.

• Do this with all the lines.

• The player with the most points wins.

Homework/Review 2

A How do you get a mouse to fly?

Use a copy of this box.

5.93	0.9	1.9		0.84	6.04		5.78	
			E					E
5.87	1.13	5.78	0.05	0.4		6.04	0.84	1.3	0.5	0.4	6.04

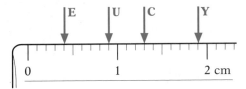

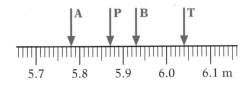

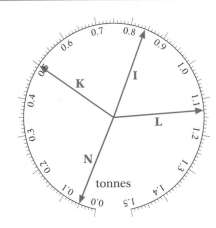

B Shana worked on a farm.

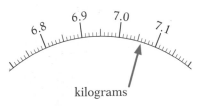

1. She weighed a new-born lamb.

   How much did it weigh?

2. She measured its height.

   How high is it?

◀◀ CHAPTER REVIEW ◀◀

◀◀
Exercise 3
on page 251

A | km   m   cm   mm   tonne   kg   g   *l*   m*l* |

Which unit would these be measured in?
Choose from the box.

1. how far it is from London to Los Angeles
2. the weight of coal taken from a mine in a month.
3. the height of Mount Everest
4. how much a teaspoon holds
5. the weight of a cat
6. the amount of oil used by a car in a year

◀◀
Exercise 5
on page 253

B What number goes in the gap?
Choose from the box.

| 2   20   200   2000 |

1. A petrol can could hold about _____ litres of petrol.
2. The petrol can could be about _____ cm wide.
3. A van could be about _____ metres high.

◀◀
Exercise 7
on page 255

C

The child in this picture is about 1 metre tall.
About how long is the snake?

◀◀
Exercises 8,
9 and 10 on
pages 257,
258 and 259

D What are these arrows pointing to?

1.

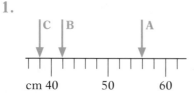

2.

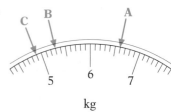

3.

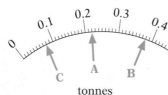

4.

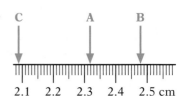

20 Directions

Getting around......................................

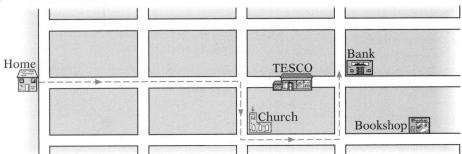

Mary went from home to the bank.
She walked out of her house,
then walked 2 streets,
turned right,
walked 1 street,
turned left,
walked 1 street,
turned left,
walked 1 street to the bank.
Write down the directions for another way Mary could have
gone to the bank.
Write down 2 different ways Mary could go to the bookshop.

North, East, South and West

Remember	The four main directions are **North**, **East**, **South** and **West**. **Due North** means exactly North. **Due East** means exactly East.		N is North. E is East. S is South. W is West.
Example	**A** is due North of **B**. **B** is due West of **C**.		

Exercise 1   Use a copy of this.
Write the missing directions on.

1.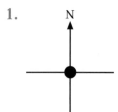

2.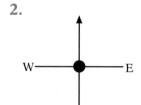

3.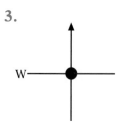

4.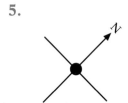

5.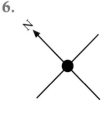

6.

Examples

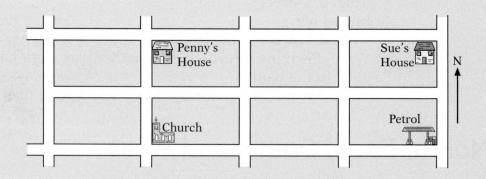

1.   Penny walked East to Sue's house.
What direction did she walk to go home?

2.   What direction is the church from Penny's house?

Answers   1.   Penny had to walk West to go home.

             2.   The church is South of Penny's house.

Exercise 2

A

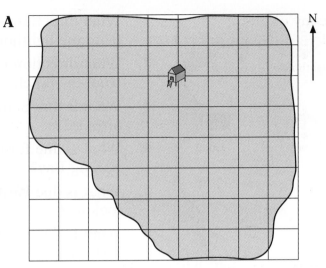

Use a copy of this.

1. There is a fox due South of the hen house.
   Put a cross at **3** places the fox could be.

2. There is a farmhouse due West of the hen house.
   Put a dot at **3** places the farmhouse could be.

B

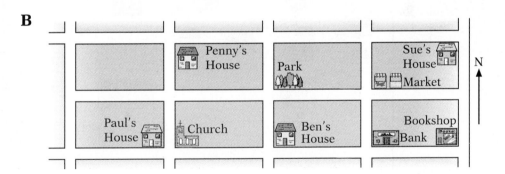

1. What direction is the market from the bank?

2. What is East of the bank?

3. What direction is the bookshop from Sue's house?

4. What direction is Ben's house from the bank?

5. What is North of Ben's house?

6. What is West of the church?

7. Penny walked East from her house.
   At the first corner she turned and walked South.
   Whose house did she go to?

C

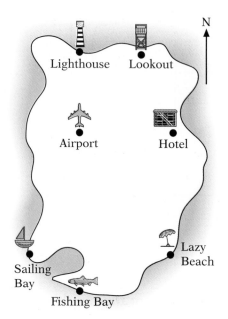

1. What direction is the airport from the lighthouse?

2. What direction is the airport from the hotel?

3. What is due South of the airport?

4. What is due East of Sailing Bay?

5. What is due West of the lookout?

6. What is due North of Lazy Beach?

7. Menna walked due East from the lighthouse. Where did she walk to?

D

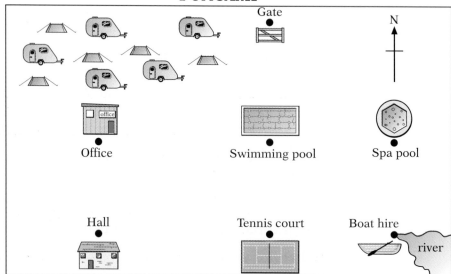

1. What direction is the swimming pool from the gate?

2. What direction is the spa pool from the boat hire?

3. Jan walked South from the swimming pool. Where did she walk to?

4. What is North of the hall?

5. What is East of the swimming pool?

6. What is West of the tennis court?

E

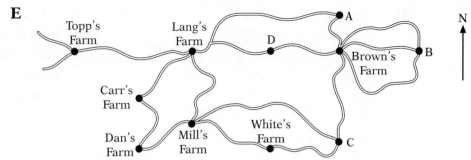

1. What direction is Mill's Farm from Lang's Farm?
2. Sam walked due East from Dan's Farm.
   Which farm did he come to?
3. Which farm is due North of Dan's Farm?
4. Which farm is due West of Lang's Farm?
5. What direction is Brown's Farm from Lang's Farm?
6. Taylor's Farm is due North of Brown's Farm.
   Which dot is it at?
7. Ming's Farm is due West of Brown's Farm.
   Which dot is it at?

F

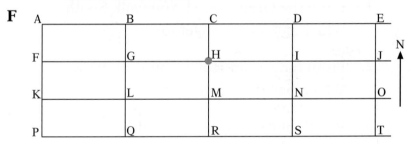

This shows some streets in New Town.
Each corner has a letter on it.

1. Stan is standing at corner H.
   He walks 1 block West, then 2 blocks South.
   What corner does he end up at?
2. He starts again from H and walks 1 block North and then
   2 blocks East.
   What corner does he end up at?
3. Stan starts at H and walks to P.
   Write down 3 ways he could go.
   Use North, South, East, West in your answer.
4. Stan starts at H and walks **two** blocks in any direction.
   Examples   1 block East and 1 block North
                or 2 blocks South
   Write down the letters of all the corners he could end up at.

G

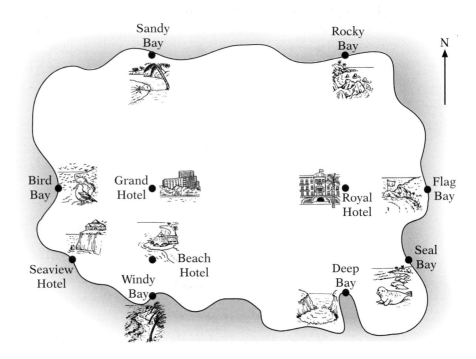

1. From the Grand Hotel, you walk South.
    Which hotel do you get to?

2. From the Grand Hotel, you walk West.
    Which bay do you get to?

3. Which bay is North of Grand Hotel?

4. What direction is Seaview Hotel from Beach Hotel?

5. What direction is Seal Bay from Beach Hotel?

6. From Beach Hotel Jon walked North to Sandy Bay.
    What direction must he now walk to get to Rocky Bay?

7. Follow these directions.
    Start at Sandy Bay.
    Go South to a bay.
    Then go East to a bay.
    Now go North to a hotel.
    Now go West to a bay.
    Which bay are you at?

H This shows some streets in Old Town.

Ben began at the dot.

He walked 2 streets East, then 1 street North.

He was then at P.

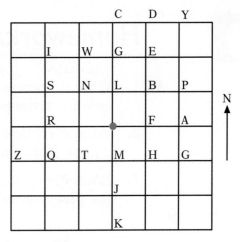

1. Write down another way he could get to P.

2. May meets a stranger at T.

    He asks May how to get to B.

    Write down 2 ways May could tell him.

3. Choose two letters on the grid.

    Write down some directions for how to get from one of the letters to the other.

Investigation

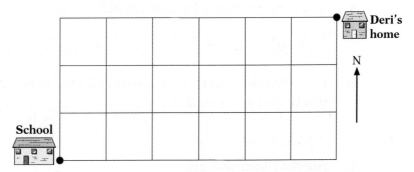

This shows the streets between Deri's home and his school.

Deri can get to school by going West 6 streets and South 3 streets.

Write down all the different ways Deri can get to school.

Homework/Review

A 1. What direction is the cafe from the playground?

2. What direction is the golf course from the cafe?

3. What is due West of the playground?

4. What is due East of the golf course?

5. Pam walked due South from the duck pond to the flower garden. Which dot is the flower garden at?

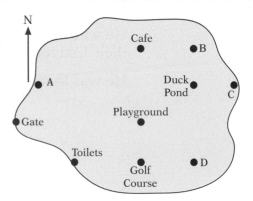

Abbot Park

B

A	B	C	D	E
F	G	H	I	J
K	L	M	N	O
P	Q	R	S	T
U	V	W	X	Y

N

This shows the streets of old York.

1. A window cleaner begins at corner W.
He works North 1 street, then West 2 streets.
What corner does he end up at?

2. Another window cleaner begins at M and ends at T.
Write down 3 ways she could go from M to T.

3. Jim's Window Cleaners always clean 2 streets each day.
Jim began at M in the morning.
Write down the letters of all the corners he could end up at by the end of the day.

4. Follow these directions.
Start at U.
Go North 3 streets.
Go East 4 streets.
Go South 2 streets.
Go West 1 street.
What corner do you end up at?

Task

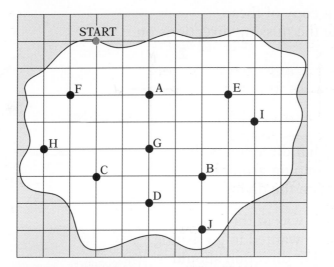

Choose which letter to bury treasure at.
Write down directions to get from the START to your treasure.

Example   Jill chose letter J.
She wrote: From the start, go East 3 squares, then
South 2 squares, then West 1 square, then South 4 squares,
then East 3 squares, then South 1 square, then West 1 square.

Puzzle

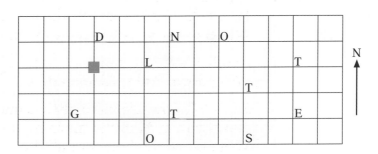

Follow this path.
Write down each letter as you come to it.
Start at ■ . Go North 1 square, East 5 squares,
West 2 squares, South 3 squares, West 4 squares,
East 9 squares, North 2 squares, West 6 squares,
South 3 squares, East 4 squares, North 2 squares.
What does the message say?

◀◀ CHAPTER REVIEW ◀◀

◀◀

Exercise 1
on page 264

A Use a copy of these.
Write the missing directions on.

1.

2.

3.

◀◀

Exercise 2
on page 265

B 1. What direction is the
camping ground
from the diving?

2. Jan was at the beach.
She wanted to go fishing.
What direction should
she walk in?

3. Stan walked South
from the beach.
Where did he go to?

4. Isaac walked East from diving.
Where did he go to?

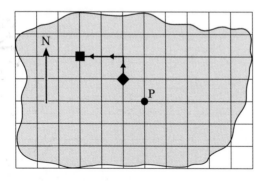

◀◀

Exercise 2
on page 265

C

Use a copy of this.
A space camera can only
move North, East, South
and West.
It starts at ◆.
It moves 1 square North
and 2 squares West.
It ends at ■.

1. The camera begins at ◆.
It moves 3 squares West and 2 squares North.
Mark the point it ends at with a ● .

2. The camera begins at P.
Mark all the points it can get to by moving 3 squares.
Use **X** to mark the points.

21 Time and Timetables

Fast or slow ....

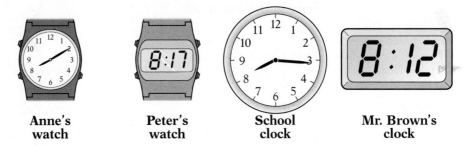

| Anne's watch | Peter's watch | School clock | Mr. Brown's clock |

What time do each of these show?
Mr Brown's clock is showing the right time.
Which clock is slow? By how much?
Which clocks are fast? By how much?

Time

Remember . . .

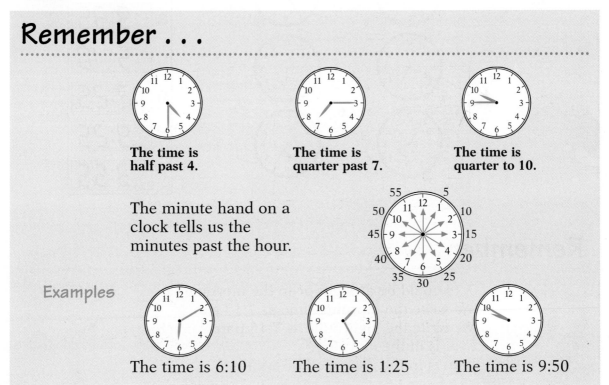

The time is half past 4.

The time is quarter past 7.

The time is quarter to 10.

The minute hand on a clock tells us the minutes past the hour.

Examples

The time is 6:10

The time is 1:25

The time is 9:50

Exercise 1

A What goes in the gaps?
The first one is done.

1. This clock shows _quarter_ past 6.
This is the same as _6:15_ .

2. This clock shows _____ past 5.
This is the same as _____ .

3. This clock shows _____ to _____ .
This is the same as _____ .

4. This clock shows _____ to _____ .
This is the same as _____ .

B Which digital time in the box shows the same time as the clock?

1.   2.

3.   4.

5.   6.

A	5:45
B	9:35
C	5:10
D	12:25
E	9:25
F	3:55

Remember . . .

7:15 could be at night or in the morning.
We write the morning time as 7:15 **a.m.**
We write the night time as 7:15 **p.m.**
a.m. is in the **morning**.
p.m. is in the **afternoon** or **evening**.

Exercise 2   Write down what time it is using a.m. or p.m.

Example   Fred took a shower.
Clock A shows the time he started.
Clock B shows the time he finished.
How many minutes did he take?

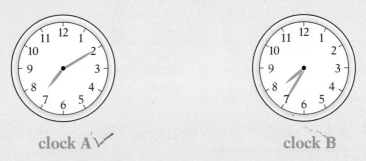

clock A ✓   clock B

Answer   The minute hand has gone around 25 minutes.
Fred took 25 minutes.

Exercise 3   **A   1.**   Ravi went to a piano lesson.
Clock A shows when it began.
Clock B shows when it ended.
How long was the lesson?

clock A   clock B

2. Cindy played a game of tennis.
Clock A shows when it began.
Clock B shows when it ended.
How long was Cindy's game?

clock A   clock B

B These clocks show the start and end times of some TV programmes.
How long was each?

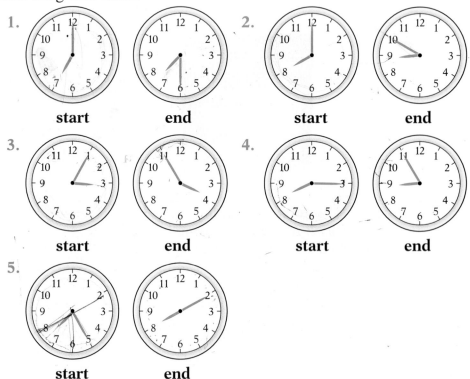

1.
start   end

2.
start   end

3.
start   end

4.
start   end

5.
start   end

Example   A film at the cinema begins at 7:35 p.m. and ends at 9:15 p.m.
How long is the film?

Answer

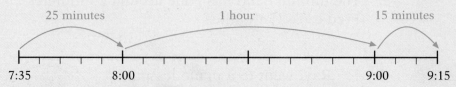

25 minutes   1 hour   15 minutes

7:35   8:00   9:00   9:15

Each dash is 5 minutes.
So altogether the film lasts 1 hour + 25 minutes + 15 minutes.
25 + 15 = 40
So the film lasts 1 hour and 40 minutes.

Exercise 4   **A**   1. Mr Chen went to the gym at 5 o'clock.
He left at 25 past 6.
How long was he there for?

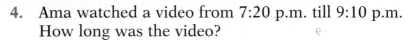

2. Mandy ordered a pizza at 6:10 p.m.
It came at 7:55 p.m.
How long did it take?

3. Tim went for a bike ride at 10:15 a.m.
He came home at 11:35 a.m.
How long did he ride for?

4. Ama watched a video from 7:20 p.m. till 9:10 p.m.
How long was the video?

5. A film starts on TV at 8:45 p.m. and ends at 11:15 p.m.
How long is the film?

B   This shows the timetable for Rick's day.

8:30	Maths begins.
9:20	Maths ends and French begins.
10:10	French ends and break begins.
10:30	Break ends and History begins.
11:20	History ends and Art begins.
12:10	Art ends and class meeting begins.
12:25	Lunch time begins.

1. How long is Maths?

2. How long is break?

3. How long is class meeting time?

4. Rick went to History at 10:39 a.m.
How many minutes late was he?

5. At 9:10 a.m. the fire alarm went.
How many minutes from the start of Maths was this?

6. The notices were read to Rick's class at 12:16 p.m.
How many minutes before lunch time was this?

7. Rick's friend went home sick at 11:15 a.m.
He came to school at 8:05 a.m.
How long had he been at school?

Example   A runner began at 10:15 a.m.
He ran for 1 hour and 25 minutes.
What time did he finish?

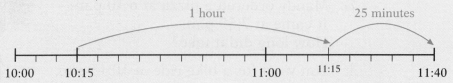

1 hour   25 minutes

10:00   10:15   11:00   11:15   11:40

Answer   Each dash is 5 minutes.
He finished at 11:40 a.m.

Exercise 5   **A**   1.   Jake wakes at 6:55 a.m. and takes 1 hour to get ready for school.
What time is he ready for school?

2.   Jenni went to her friend's house at 10:25 a.m.
She stayed for 1 hour and 10 minutes.
What time did she go home?

3.   Gary got on the train at 7:20 p.m.
He was on it for 1 hour and 35 minutes.
What time did he get off?

B   Tom's bus always takes 55 minutes to go from home to work.
What time would he get to work if he caught a bus leaving at these times?
     1.   8:30 a.m.   2.   7:50 a.m.   3.   8:10 a.m.   4.   7:35 a.m.

Puzzles

1.   A man must take one pill every half an hour starting now.
How long will it take him to have 15 pills?

2.   A batch of scones takes 11 minutes to cook.
Jan has a 3-minute and 7-minute egg timer.
How can she time the scones using these?
Hint : you need to start the timers before you put the scones in the oven.

Homework/Review 1

A Colin went for a run.
He saw these 3 clocks.
What goes in the gaps?

1. The first clock reads
   _____ past _____ .
   This is the same as _____ .

2. The next clock reads _____ to _____ .
   This is the same as _____ .

3. The last clock reads _____ to _____ .
   This is the same as _____ .

B Colin got home from his run and had dinner at 6:25.
Write this as a.m. or p.m. time.

C The next week Colin went for 2 more runs.
These clocks show the start and end times of these.
How long was each?

1.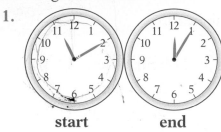

    start   end

2.

    start   end

D 1. Colin put a chocolate cake in the oven at 4:40 p.m.
   He took it out at 5:20 p.m.
   How long did it cook for?

   2. Colin watched a film. It began at
   9:30 p.m. and finished at 12:10 a.m.
   How long was the film?

E 1. Colin went for a run at 10:55 a.m.
   He was away for 1 hour and 15 minutes.
   What time did he get back?

   2. Colin went shopping after his run.
   He left at 1:25 p.m. and was away for 2 hours and 40 minutes.
   When did he get back?

24-hour time

There are 24 hours from midnight one day to midnight the next.
a.m./p.m. time has two lots of 12 hours.

| midnight | | | | | a.m. | | | | | | noon | | | | | p.m. | | | | | midnight |
| 12 | 1 | 2 | 3 | 4 | 5 | 6 | 7 | 8 | 9 | 10 | 11 | 12 | 1 | 2 | 3 | 4 | 5 | 6 | 7 | 8 | 9 | 10 | 11 | 12 |

Some clocks go up to 24.
They don't start at 1 o'clock again after noon.

The times along the bottom are 24-hour times.
24-hour times always have **4** numbers.

Examples   1 p.m. is 13:00   2 p.m. is 14:00   3 p.m. is 15:00
9 a.m. is 09:00   2 a.m. is 02:00
8:20 a.m. is 08:20   6:25 p.m. is 18:25

Sometimes 24-hour time is written with no dots.

Example   08:20 is written as 0820.

Exercise 6   **A**   Write these times as 24-hour times.

1. 7 a.m.
2. 5 a.m.
3. 1 p.m.
4. 6 p.m.
5. 10 p.m.
6. 2 a.m.
7. 11 p.m.
8. 12 p.m.
9. 9:45 p.m.
10. 4:15 p.m.
11. 11:14 p.m.
12. 10:20 a.m.
13. 5:25 p.m.
14. 7:55 p.m.
15. 9:16 p.m.
16. 1:50 p.m.
17. 11:35 a.m.
18. 2:35 p.m.
19. 7:16 p.m.
20. 5:40 p.m.
21. 12:05 a.m.
22. seventeen minutes past midnight
23. quarter to eleven in the morning
24. ten past eight at night
25. twenty to four in the afternoon
26. eight thirty five at night
27. five to eleven at night
28. ten fifty two in the morning

B Write these as a.m. or p.m. times.

1.	04:00	**2.**	06:00	**3.**	09:00	**4.**	11:00
5.	10:15	**6.**	13:00	**7.**	15:00	**8.**	18:00
9.	22:00	**10.**	20:00	**11.**	19:00	**12.**	21:15
13.	12:30	**14.**	02:05	**15.**	14:10	**16.**	16:35
17.	20:55	**18.**	23:45	**19.**	22:07	**20.**	13:09
21.	23:59	**22.**	18:47	**23.**	19:38	**24.**	19:16
25.	21:17	**26.**	01:01	**27.**	00:16	**28.**	00:35
29.	00:47	**30.**	19:19	**31.**	20:02		

C Write the times on these clocks as 24-hour times.

1. afternoon

2. morning

3. afternoon

4. morning

5. afternoon

Exercise 7

These signs were at Tom's local shops.

BUTCHER

open Mon–Sat
0800 – 1730

CAFE

open between
1630 and 2230

LIBRARY

open 1030 to 1800

return books in slot
at other times

1. Milly went to the butcher's on the way home from work.
    She got there at 5:45 p.m.
    Was the butcher open?

2. How many hours is the cafe open each day?

3. Tom took a book back to the library at 6:30 p.m.
    Did he have to use the slot?

4. Tom wanted to have tea at the cafe at 5:30 p.m.
    Was it open?

Timetables

Timetables usually give the times as 24-hour times.
They are usually written without dots.

Example

Bus timetable – Teston to Hadlow				
Teston departs	0652	0750	0922	1022
Hadlow arrives	0709	0809	0941	1041

This timetable gives the times as 24-hour times.
The bus that leaves Teston at 0750 arrives at Hadlow at 0809.

Exercise 8   **A**   Use the timetable above to answer these questions.

1. Sally caught the **0922** bus from Teston.
    What time does she arrive at Hadlow?

2. How many minutes does the journey take?

3. Dan caught the **0750** bus from Teston.
    He had to wait 15 minutes at the bus stop.
    What time did he get to the bus stop?

4. Do all the buses take the same time to go from Teston to
    Hadlow?

B

Train timetable – London to Hull						
London departs	06:00	07:30	08:20	09:30	10:10	14:30
Hull arrives	09:22	10:29	11:26	12:19	13:28	17:27

1. Bea caught the **08:20** train from London.
    What time does it arrive in Hull?

2. Sam caught the **06:00** train from London.
    How long does it take to get to Hull?

3. Sam left home at 05:25 to catch the **06:00** train.
    It takes him 25 minutes to get to the station.
    How long did he have to wait for the train?

4. How long does the **08:20** train take to get to Hull?

5. Which train takes the longest time to get to Hull?

C

Train timetable – Luton to Blackfriars					
Luton	14:00	14:30	15:18	16:04	17:11
Blackfriars	14:47	15:17	16:10	16:54	18:02

1. Gemma caught the **15:18** train from Luton.
   What time did it arrive in Blackfriars?
   Write your answer as a.m. or p.m. time.

2. How long does the train that leaves Luton at **14:00** take to get to Blackfriars?

3. Bill arrives 10 minutes too late for the **14:00** train.
   How long must he wait for the next train?

4. Rita must get to Blackfriars by 4:30 p.m.
   What trains could she catch?

5. Ravi arrives at the station at 2:05 p.m.
   How long must he wait to catch a train to Blackfriars?

6. Sari caught the **16:04** train.
   She took 14 minutes to get from her house to the station.
   She waited 10 minutes for the train to come.
   What time did she leave her house?

7. Which train takes the longest to get from Luton to Blackfriars?

D

Train timetable – Guildford to Reading							
Guildford	0654	0736	0759	0904	1004	then every	1604
Reading	0751	0836	0852	0949	1049	hour until	1649

1. Derek caught the **0759** train from Guildford to Reading.
   What time does it arrive in Reading?

2. How many minutes does it take?

3. All the trains between **0904** and **1504** take the same time.
   What time will the **1404** train arrive in Reading?

4. Ruth wants to be in Reading after 10 a.m. but before 2 p.m.
   What trains could Ruth catch?

Homework/Review 2

A What has 22 legs and goes CRUNCH CRUNCH CRUNCH?

| 4:25 p.m. | 3:25 p.m. | 10:25 p.m. | 10:25 p.m. | 07:30 ᵀ | 00:25 | 4:25 p.m. | 8:25 p.m. | 8:25 p.m. |

07:30 ᵀ 8:25 a.m. 4:25 p.m. 19:30   8:25 a.m. 4:25 p.m. 07:30 ᵀ 17:35 15:35 05:35

7:25 p.m. 12:25 17:35 1:25 a.m. 12:25 a.m. 1:25 a.m.

Use a copy of this box.
What are these as 24-hour times?

| **T** | 7:30 a.m. | **M** | 7:30 p.m. | **R** | 12:25 p.m. | **B** | 12:25 a.m. |
| **G** | 5:35 a.m. | **I** | 5:35 p.m. | **N** | 3:35 p.m. | | |

What are these as a.m. or p.m. times?

| **L** | 20:25 | **A** | 16:25 | **E** | 08:25 | **O** | 22:25 |
| **F** | 15:25 | **S** | 01:25 | **P** | 00:25 | **C** | 19:25 |

B Colin got this notice from his running club.
   1. Write 1415 as a.m. or p.m. time.
   2. What time in a.m. or p.m. time does the dance start and end?
   3. How long is the dance?
   4. What time does Colin have to be at the club on Sunday if he wants to run?
       Give your answer in 24-hour time.

> **RUNNING CLUB**
> Run this Sun 1415 at the club
> Runners be there 20 minutes before start
> **Dance Sat Night 1930 – 2300**

C

Plane timetable – Dublin to London					
Dublin	0725	0855	1055	then every	1955
London	0835	1005	1205	hour until	2105

   1. Ken caught the **0725** plane from Dublin to London.
       What time did he arrive in London?
   2. Ken's sister went to the airport at 8:15 a.m. to meet him.
       How long did she have to wait?
   3. Each plane from **1055** to **1955** takes the same time to fly from Dublin to London.
       What time will the **1655** plane be in London?
   4. Julie wants to be in London after 10 a.m. but before 12 p.m.
       Which plane should she catch?

Task

• •

You will need pencil and paper
a copy of this

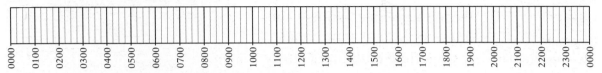

Choose a day of your life.
Colour the chart to show what you did.
Write down what each colour means.

Example

Jo coloured the part from 1530 to 1700 in blue.
She wrote:
Blue – played tennis.

◀◀ CHAPTER REVIEW ◀◀

◀◀

Exercises 1
and 2 on
pages 274
and 275

A Amy went swimming on Sunday morning.
The clock at the pool is shown.
1. The clock shows _____ to _____ .
2. Which of these shows the same time as
the clock at the pool?

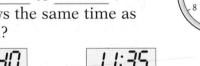

| 10:25 | 10:40 | 11:35 | 10:35 |
| A | B | C | D |

3. Write the time as a.m. or p.m. time.

◀◀

Exercises 3
and 4 on
pages 275
and 277

B 1. Shana went for a ride on her horse.
These watches show when she left and when she came back.

 left  came back

How long was her ride?
2. The next day she left for her ride at 10:50 a.m.
She came back at 12:35 p.m.
How long did she ride for?

Exercise 5
on page 278

C 1. Tony went to Pizza Hut with his friends at 7:25 p.m.
He stayed there for 2 hours and 15 minutes.
What time did he leave?

2. Tina left for her Grandmother's at 10:45 a.m.
It took 1 hour and 45 minutes to get there.
What time did she get there?

Exercise 6
on page 280

D Write these East Tennis Club times as a.m. or p.m. times.

1. the time club night starts

2. the time club night ends

3. the times the club is open during the day

EAST TENNIS CLUB
Club Night
Wed 1800 – 2030
Open Daily
1015 – 1430
1715 – 2100

Exercise 6
on page 280

E Write these West Tennis Club times as 24-hour times.

1. the time club night starts

2. the time club night ends

3. the times the club is open during the day

WEST TENNIS CLUB
Club Night
Thur 6:30 – 8:00
Open For Games
every day
11 a.m. – 4:30 p.m.

Exercise 7
on page 281

F Use the tennis club notices in **D** and **E** to answer these.

1. Brian arrived at East Tennis Club at 3:30 p.m.
Was it open?

2. How many hours is East Tennis Club open each day other than Wednesday?

3. Brian finishes work at 5 p.m.
He likes to play tennis on his way home.
Which club is he best to join?

Exercise 8
on page 282

G

Train timetable – London to Stroud					
London	05:50	11:30	14:15	17:03	18:18
Stroud	07:45	12:48	15:49	18:29	19:46

1. Tom caught the **14:15** train from London.
What time did it reach Stroud?
Give your answer in a.m. or p.m. time.

2. Tom's sister wants to be in Stroud after 9 a.m. but before 2:30 p.m.
Which train should she catch?

3. Which train takes the longest?
How long does it take?

Quick Test 7

Mr. and Mrs. Brown went on holiday.

A The hotel is about 9 m high. About how high are these?
1. diving board
2. tree
3. trampoline

B Mr. and Mrs. Brown had to go on the ferry.
Some cars were measured before they went on the ferry.

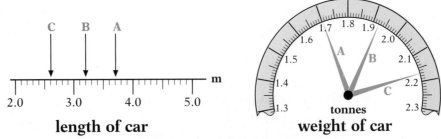

length of car   **weight of car**

1. How long are each of the cars?
2. How much do each of the cars weigh?

C

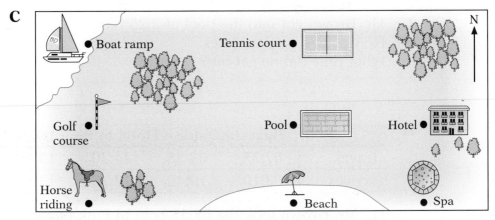

These are the hotel grounds where Mr. and Mrs. Brown stayed.
1. What direction is the golf course from the pool?
2. What direction is the pool from the beach?
3. What is West of the beach?
4. What is South of the golf course?
5. Mrs. Brown walked East from the pool.
   Where did she walk to?
   What direction must she then walk in to go to the spa?

D These clocks show the
meal times at the hotel.

breakfast   lunch   tea
starts   starts   starts

Write these times as
a.m. or p.m. times.

1. start of breakfast
2. start of lunch
3. start of tea

E Use the clocks in **D**.
Write these times as 24-hour times.

1. start of breakfast
2. start of lunch
3. start of tea

F Mrs. Brown got into the spa at 06:55.
She got out at 08:10.
How long was she in the spa?

G Mr. Brown got into the pool at 2:25 p.m.
He was in for 45 minutes.
What time did he get out?

H

Boat timetable – Hotel to Pink Island					
leaves	07:25	09:55	11:30	13:10	14:50
arrives	08:10	10:40	12:15	13:55	15:35

1. Mr. Brown took the **09:55** boat to Pink Island.
   What time did it arrive?

2. Mrs. Brown wanted to be at Pink Island after 9:30 a.m. but
   before 2:30 p.m.
   Which boats could she catch?

3. Each boat takes the same time.
   An extra boat left at 10:25.
   What time did it arrive at Pink Island?

Paving ....

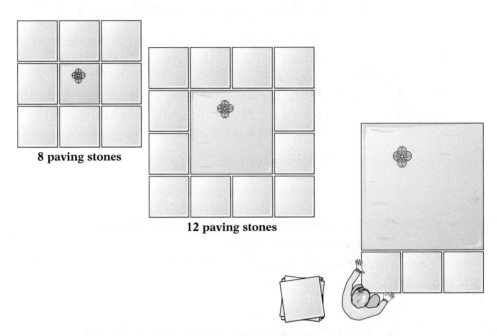

8 paving stones

12 paving stones

How many paving stones will fit around a pond that is 3 paving stones wide?

Rules in words

Example Gavin worked out his wages like this.

Multiply the number of hours worked by 5.

Gavin worked 7 hours on Saturday.
His wages are $7 \times 5 = £35$.

Exercise 1 **A** Pip worked in a hire firm.
She worked out the cost to hire a trailer like this.

Cost is the number of hours hired times £3.

How much does it cost to hire a trailer for
1. 3 hours   2. 5 hours   3. 4 hours?

B The cost to hire a box of wine glasses is found like this.

Multiply the number of days hired by £5.

How much would it cost to hire the glasses for
1. 1 day   2. 2 days   3. 4 days   4. 5 days?

C The cost to hire a ladder is found like this.

Multiply the number of days hired by £4.

How much would it cost to hire the ladder for
1. 3 days   2. 8 days   3. 10 days   4. 14 days?

Example A cleaner in an office building worked out how many hours each job would take like this.

Multiply the number of floors by 2 and subtract 1.

How many hours would it take to clean 4 floors?

Answer First we multiply the number of floors by 2.

$4 \times 2 = 8$
Then subtract 1.
$8 - 1 = 7$

It would take 7 hours.

Exercise 2   **A**

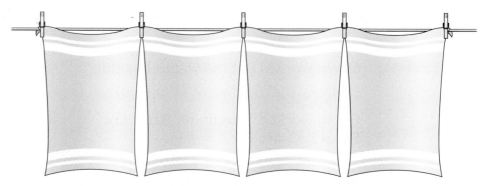

Jim hung his towels on the line like this.
The number of pegs needed is given by

the number of towels plus one.

How many pegs are needed for
1. 1 towel   2. 5 towels   3. 8 towels   4. 16 towels?

B   The amount a car sales person is paid each week is given by

number of cars sold × £100 + £150

How much would the sales person earn in a week when these numbers of cars were sold?

    1.   1 car   **2.**   4 cars   **3.**   0 cars   **4.**   6 cars

C   A recipe for cooking lamb gives the cooking time as

the number of kg times 40 minutes plus 20 minutes more.

How long would it take to cook lamb that weighed

    1.   2 kg   **2.**   3 kg   **3.**   4 kg?

D

    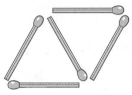   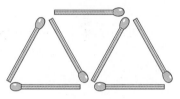

    1 triangle   **2 triangles**   **3 triangles**

This is a matchstick pattern.
The number of matchsticks needed for each pattern is given by

multiply the number of triangles by 2 and add 1.

Use the rule to work out how many matchsticks will be needed for a pattern with

    1.   4 triangles   **2.**   6 triangles   **3.**   7 triangles
    4.   9 triangles   **5.**   10 triangles.

E   Julie made matchstick space people for her little sister.

    1 matchstick tall   **2 matchsticks tall**   **3 matchsticks tall**

The number of matchsticks needed for each space person is given by

multiply the number of matchsticks tall by 3 and add 4.

Use the rule to work out how many matchsticks will be needed for a space person that is

    1.   4 matchsticks tall   **2.**   8 matchsticks tall.

Example   A number machine multiplies numbers by 3 and adds 1.

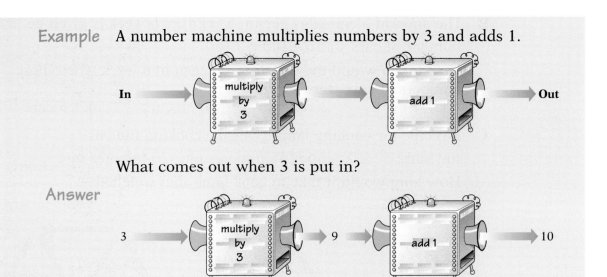

What comes out when 3 is put in?

Answer

Exercise 3   **A**   This number machine multiplies numbers by 2.

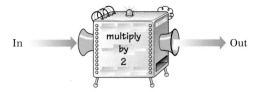

What number will come out when these are put in?
1. 4   2. 10   3. 20   4. 50

B   Write down the numbers that will come out of these number machines.

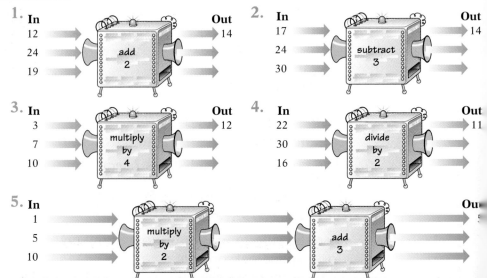

6.

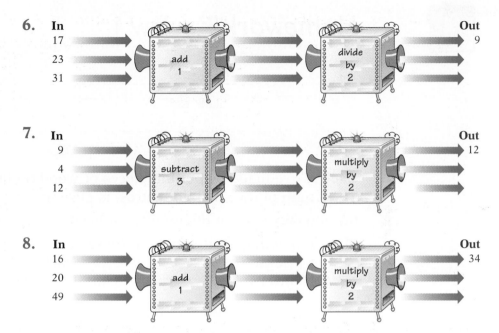

7.

8.

Puzzles

1. Sam is 5 years younger than Val.
Val is 10.
How old will Sam be in 2 years time?

2. Sally is 4 years older than Dan.
Dan is 7.
How old will Sally be in 5 years time?

3. Write down any number.
Multiply it by 3.
Add 6.
Divide by 3.
Subtract the number you first wrote down.
What is your answer?

Do this again for some different numbers.

Homework/Review 1

A

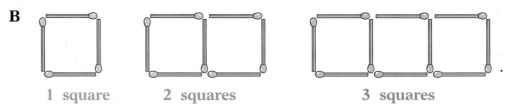

1 metre   2 metres

3 metres

Shelves are made by putting pieces of wood on bricks.
The length of the shelf, in metres, is given by
take one away from the number of bricks.
How long will a shelf sitting on these be?
  1. 5 bricks   2. 9 bricks
  3. 15 bricks   4. 17 bricks

B

1 square   2 squares   3 squares

This is a matchstick pattern.
The number of matchsticks needed for each pattern is given by
multiply the number of squares by 3 and add 1.

Use the rule to work out how many matchsticks are needed for a
pattern with
  1. 5 squares   2. 8 squares   3. 10 squares.

C Use a copy of this.
Fill in the numbers that will come out.

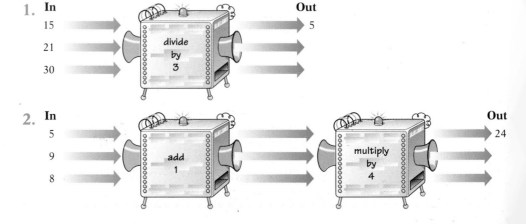

1. **In**   **Out**
    15   5
    21   divide
                    by
    30   3

2. **In**   **Out**
    5   24
    9   add   multiply
                    1   by
    8   4

Number patterns

There are number patterns all around us.
The houses on one side of a street have these numbers.

This is the number pattern of **even** numbers.
This number pattern has the rule **add two**.

The houses on the other side of the street have these numbers.

This is the number pattern of **odd** numbers.
It also has the rule **add two**.

Why does the same rule give a different pattern this time?

Remember   ... means the number pattern carries on.

Example   3, 6, 9, 12, 15, 18, ...

The rule for 3, 6, 9, 12, 15, 18, ... is **add 3**.

To find the next number we add 3 to 18.
18 + 3 = 21. The next number is 21.
To find the number after this we add 3 to 21.
21 + 3 = 24. The next number is 24.

Exercise 4

1. 5, 10, 15, 20, 25, ...
   The rule for this number pattern is **add 5**.
   Find the next 3 numbers.

2. 1, 4, 7, 10, 13, ...
   The rule for this number pattern is **add 3**.
   Find the next 3 numbers.

3.   4, 5, 7, ...

The rule for this number pattern is
multiply by 2 and subtract 3.

Find the next 3 numbers.

4.   5, 6, 8, ...

The rule for this number pattern is
subtract 2 and multiply by 2.

Find the next 3 numbers.

Example   This is a number chain.

$1 \rightarrow 3 \rightarrow 5 \rightarrow 7 \rightarrow 9 \rightarrow 11 \rightarrow 13 \rightarrow$

The rule is **add on 2**.

What is the rule for this number chain?
$1 \rightarrow 3 \rightarrow 9 \rightarrow 27 \rightarrow$

Answer   We have to work out what is done each time to get the next
number.

Each number has been multiplied by 3.
So the rule is **multiply by 3**.

Exercise 5   **A**   A rule is given.
Use the rule to work out the next 3 numbers in the chain.

1.   add three $2 \rightarrow 5 \rightarrow \square \rightarrow \square \rightarrow \square \rightarrow$

2.   multiply by 2 $3 \rightarrow 6 \rightarrow \square \rightarrow \square \rightarrow \square \rightarrow$

3.   subtract 5 $50 \rightarrow 45 \rightarrow \square \rightarrow \square \rightarrow \square \rightarrow$

4.   multiply by 2 and add 1 $1 \rightarrow 3 \rightarrow \square \rightarrow \square \rightarrow \square \rightarrow$

5.   subtract 1 and multiply by 2 $5 \rightarrow 8 \rightarrow \square \rightarrow \square \rightarrow \square \rightarrow$

6.   multiply by 2 and subtract 3 $3 \rightarrow 3 \rightarrow \square \rightarrow \square \rightarrow \square \rightarrow$

7.   multiply by 2 and subtract 3 $5 \rightarrow 7 \rightarrow \square \rightarrow \square \rightarrow \square \rightarrow$

8.   multiply by 2 and add 3 $1 \rightarrow 5 \rightarrow \square \rightarrow \square \rightarrow \square \rightarrow$

B   Work out the rules for these number chains.

1. $2 \rightarrow 4 \rightarrow 6 \rightarrow 8 \rightarrow 10 \rightarrow$

2. $1 \rightarrow 5 \rightarrow 9 \rightarrow 13 \rightarrow 17 \rightarrow$

3. $1 \rightarrow 2 \rightarrow 4 \rightarrow 8 \rightarrow 16 \rightarrow$

4. $5 \rightarrow 10 \rightarrow 15 \rightarrow 20 \rightarrow 25 \rightarrow$

5. $10 \rightarrow 9 \rightarrow 8 \rightarrow 7 \rightarrow 6 \rightarrow$

6. $200 \rightarrow 100 \rightarrow 50 \rightarrow 25 \rightarrow$

7. $20 \rightarrow 17 \rightarrow 14 \rightarrow 11 \rightarrow 8 \rightarrow$

8. $1 \rightarrow 5 \rightarrow 25 \rightarrow 125 \rightarrow 625 \rightarrow$

Example   A number chain begins as $2 \rightarrow 6 \rightarrow$
We could carry this on in many ways.

One rule could be **multiply by 3**.
The chain would be $2 \rightarrow 6 \rightarrow 18 \rightarrow 54 \rightarrow 162 \rightarrow$

Another rule could be **multiply by 2 and add 2**.
The chain would be $2 \rightarrow 6 \rightarrow 14 \rightarrow 30 \rightarrow 62 \rightarrow$

Another rule could be **multiply by 4 and subtract 2**.
The chain would be $2 \rightarrow 6 \rightarrow 22 \rightarrow 86 \rightarrow 342 \rightarrow$

There are many rules that could give a chain
that begins $2 \rightarrow 6 \rightarrow$

Exercise 6   Write down 3 different ways to carry these number chains on.
Write down the rules you are using.
Write down the next 3 numbers.
The answer to the first one might be:

The rule is **add 3** $1 \rightarrow 4 \rightarrow 7 \rightarrow 10 \rightarrow 13$
The rule is **multiply by 4** $1 \rightarrow 4 \rightarrow 16 \rightarrow 64 \rightarrow 256$
The rule is **multiply by 3 and add 1** $1 \rightarrow 4 \rightarrow 13 \rightarrow 40 \rightarrow 121$

1. $1 \rightarrow 4$ 2. $1 \rightarrow 5$ 3. $1 \rightarrow 3$

4. $3 \rightarrow 6$ 5. $4 \rightarrow 8$ 6. $3 \rightarrow 9$

7. $3 \rightarrow 5$ 8. $2 \rightarrow 5$ 9. $1 \rightarrow 1$

Example This number line shows
a number pattern.
The numbers go up in
steps of 10.

The next 3 numbers
are 40, 50 and 60.

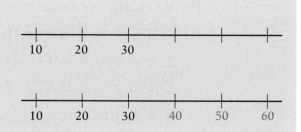

Exercise 7   **A** What goes in the gap?

1. The numbers go up in steps of _____ .
12 14 16 18 20

2. The numbers go up in steps of _____ .
30 40 50 60 70

3. The numbers go up in steps of _____ .
0 3 6 9 12

4. The numbers go up in steps of _____ .
−10 0 10 20 30

5. The numbers go up in steps of _____ .
−4 0 4 8 12

B Use a copy of this.
Fill in the missing numbers.

1.
40 50 60 __ __ __

2.
30 __ __ __ 70 80

3.
20 40 __ __ __ 120

4.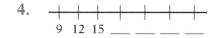
9 12 15 __ __ __ __

5.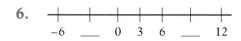
−30 −20 __ __ __ 20 30

6.
−6 __ 0 3 6 __ 12

7.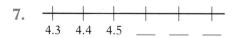
4.3 4.4 4.5 __ __ __

8.
3.6 3.7 3.8 __ __ __

9.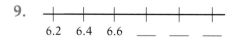
6.2 6.4 6.6 __ __ __

Investigation

You will need   some squared paper

We can make patterns by doing the same thing over and over again.

Example   Draw a line **2** squares long.
Turn 1 right angle clockwise.
Draw a line **3** squares long.
Turn 1 right angle clockwise.
Draw a line **1** square long.
Turn 1 right angle clockwise.

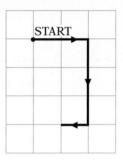

If we do this over and over
we get this pattern.
We could call this
pattern **2, 3, 1**.

Draw these patterns
over and over.

1, 2, 3,	6, 1, 5
3, 6, 2,	3, 4, 1, 2
3, 2, 5,	4, 5, 1, 3, 1

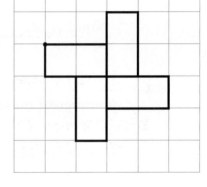

Try and work out how this
pattern has been made.

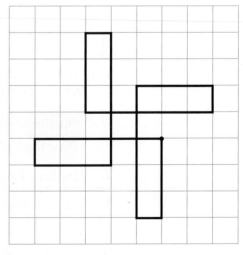

Finding rules for patterns

Example

   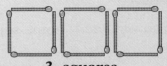

1 square   **2 squares**   **3 squares**

Number of squares	Number of matchsticks
1	4
2	8
3	12
4	___

The number of matchsticks used is **4 times** the number of squares.
So 4 squares would use $4 \times 4 = 16$ matchsticks.

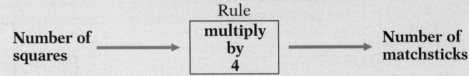

We can also write this as

Number of matchsticks = Number of squares × 4.

Exercise 8

A

1 triangle   **2 triangles**   **3 triangles**

This is a matchstick pattern.
1. What are the missing numbers on this table?

Number of triangles	1	2	3	4	5
Number of matchsticks	3	6	9	___	___

2. Explain how you got these missing numbers.

3. What is the rule for the number of matchsticks?

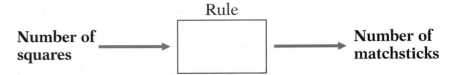

B Plant boxes are made from lengths of wood.
The dots show where they are joined.

 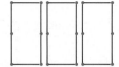

1 plant box   **2 plant boxes**   **3 plant boxes**

1. What is the missing number on this table?

2. Explain how you worked out this number.

3. Finish this rule for finding the number of lengths of wood needed.

Number of plant boxes	Number of lengths of wood
1	6
2	12
3	18
4	___

Number of lengths of wood = Number of plant boxes × ____ .

C Ben always makes his fields the same shape but different sizes.
The dots show where the fence posts are.

 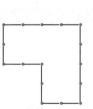 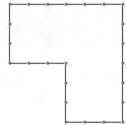

Field size 1   **Field size 2**   **Field size 3**

1. What is the missing number on this table?

2. Explain how you got this number.

3. What rule goes in the box?

Field size	Number of fence posts
1	8
2	16
3	24
4	___

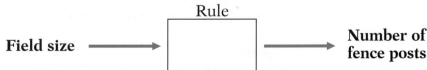

Rule

Field size ⟶ [   ] ⟶ **Number of fence posts**

4. Finish this rule.

Number of fence posts = Field size _____ .

D   Ama makes bags.
She puts a pattern on each using strips of ribbon.

1 bag   **2 bags**   **3 bags**

1.   What are the missing numbers on this table?

Number of bags	Number of strips of ribbon
1	4
2	8
3	___
4	___
5	___

2.   What rule goes in the box?

Rule

Number of bags → [   ] → **Number of strips of ribbon**

3.   Finish this rule for the number of strips of ribbon.
Number of strips of ribbon = Number of bags _____ .

E   Eve made this matchstick pattern.

1 house   **2 houses**   **3 houses**

1.   What are the missing numbers on this table?

Number of houses	Number of matchsticks
1	___
2	12
3	___
4	___
5	___

2.   What rule goes in the box?

Rule

Number of houses → [   ] → **Number of matchsticks**

3.   Finish this rule for the number of matchsticks.
Number of matchsticks = Number of houses _____ .

Homework/Review 2

A Work out the rule for these number chains.

1. $1 \rightarrow 3 \rightarrow 9 \rightarrow 27 \rightarrow 81 \rightarrow$
2. $28 \rightarrow 24 \rightarrow 20 \rightarrow 16 \rightarrow 12 \rightarrow$
3. $800 \rightarrow 400 \rightarrow 200 \rightarrow 100 \rightarrow 50 \rightarrow$

B 1. Beth made a number chain using the rule **subtract 3**.
        The first 2 numbers were $30 \rightarrow 27 \rightarrow$
        Copy and finish Beth's number chain so it has 5 numbers.
     2. Mark made a number chain using the rule
        add 1 and multiply by 2.
        The first 2 numbers were $3 \rightarrow 8 \rightarrow$
        Copy and finish Mark's number chain so it has 5 numbers.
     3. Toby made a different rule.
        His number chain also started $3 \rightarrow 8 \rightarrow$
        What might Toby's rule have been?
        How would his number chain carry on?

C Use a copy of this. Fill in the missing numbers.

D Sam made this matchstick pattern.

1 star   **2 stars**   **3 stars**

1. What are the missing numbers on this table?

Number of stars	1	2	3	4	5
Number of matchsticks	10	20	__	__	__

2. What rule goes in the box?

Rule

**Number
of stars** $\longrightarrow$ ⬚ $\longrightarrow$ **Number of
matchsticks**

3. Finish this on your copy.
    Number of matchsticks = number of stars × _____ .

Investigation

You will need a calculator

A
$3 \times 11 = 33$
$33 \times 11 = 363$
$333 \times 11 = 3663$
$3333 \times 11 = 36663$

What do you think the answer to 33333×11 will be?

Check using your calculator.

$33 \times 101 = 3333$
$333 \times 101 = 33633$
$3333 \times 101 = 336633$

What do you think the answer to 33333×101 will be?

Check using your calculator.

B Try and write down the next 2 lines of these patterns, without using your calculator.

1. $2 \times 3 = 6$
$22 \times 3 = 66$
$222 \times 3 = 666$
$2222 \times 3 = 6666$

2. $9 \times 6 = 54$
$99 \times 66 = 6534$
$999 \times 666 = 665334$
$9999 \times 6666 = 66653334$

3. $9 \times 5 = 45$
$99 \times 55 = 5445$
$999 \times 555 = 554445$
$9999 \times 5555 = 55544445$

4. $9 \times 9 = 81$
$99 \times 99 = 9801$
$999 \times 999 = 998001$
$9999 \times 9999 = 99980001$

C The number 10010 is special.
Multiply it by **any** 2-digit number.
What do you get?

D Multiply each of these numbers by 37.

3, 6, 9, 12, 15, 18, 21, 24, 27, ...

What do you get?

◀◀ CHAPTER REVIEW ◀◀

◀◀
Exercise 1
on page 289

A Jane was building
a fence.
She worked out the
cost in pounds like this.
**Multiply the length of the
fence, in metres, by 25.**
How much would it cost for a fence of

1. 4 metres   　 2. 3 metres   　 3. 10 metres?

◀◀
Exercise 2
on page 290

B She worked out how many rails she needed like this.
Multiply the number of posts by 5 then subtract 5.
How many rails would she need for a fence with this many
posts?

1. 6 posts   　 2. 8 posts   　 3. 7 posts   　 4. 10 posts

◀◀
Exercise 3
on page 292

C What numbers come out of these number machines?

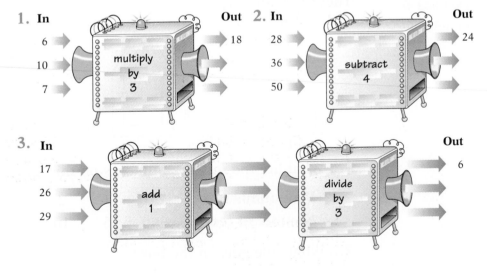

◀◀
Exercise 4
on page 295

D 9, 10, 12, 16, ...
The rule for this number pattern is
subtract 4 and multiply by 2.
Find the next 3 numbers.

◀◀
Exercise 5
on page 296

E Work out the rules for these number chains.
1. $3 \rightarrow 5 \rightarrow 7 \rightarrow 9 \rightarrow 11 \rightarrow$
2. $1 \rightarrow 2 \rightarrow 4 \rightarrow 8 \rightarrow 16 \rightarrow$
3. $24 \rightarrow 22 \rightarrow 20 \rightarrow 18 \rightarrow 16 \rightarrow$

◀◀
Exercise 6
on page 297

F Penny started a number chain like this. $2 \rightarrow 4$
Find 3 different ways to carry this pattern on.
What goes in the gaps for the number chain and the rule?

The rule is _____ $2 \rightarrow 4 \rightarrow \square \rightarrow \square \rightarrow \square$

The rule is _____ $2 \rightarrow 4 \rightarrow \square \rightarrow \square \rightarrow \square$

The rule is _____ $2 \rightarrow 4 \rightarrow \square \rightarrow \square \rightarrow \square$

◀◀
Exercise 7
on page 298

G Use a copy of this.
Fill in the missing numbers.

1.
   15   20   25   ___   ___   ___

2.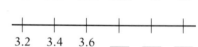
   −40   ___   ___   ___   40   60

3.
   8.6   8.7   8.8   ___   ___   ___

4.
   3.2   3.4   3.6   ___   ___   ___

◀◀
Exercise 8
on page 300

H Pool Land made pools like these.
They were all fenced.

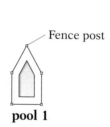

Fence post

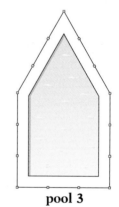

pool 1   **pool 2**   **pool 3**

1. What are the missing numbers on this table?

Pool number	1	2	3	4	5
Number of fence posts	5	10	___	___	___

2. What rule goes in the box?

Pool number → [Rule] → **Number of fence posts**

3. Finish this rule.
    Number of fence posts = Pool number × _____ .

23 Solids. Volume

Making models..

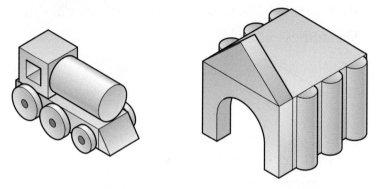

Claire made these models for the school fair.
Name the solids she has used.

Solids

Remember . . .

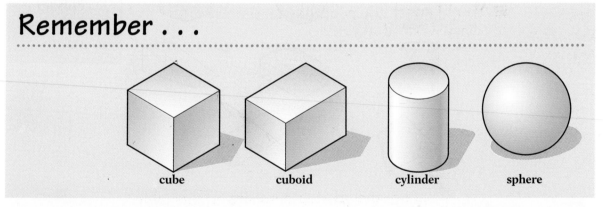

cube   cuboid   cylinder   sphere

These shapes are called **pyramids**.

All the faces except the base meet at a point.

This pyramid has a triangle as its base.

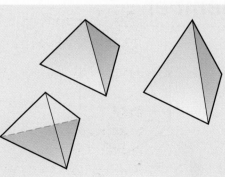

These shapes are called **prisms**.

The end faces of a prism are congruent (exactly the same).

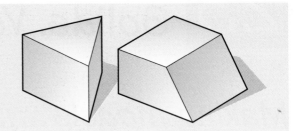

A Name these solids.

1.

2.

3.

4.

5.

6.

B Name each of these solids. Choose the name from the box.

A	sphere
B	pyramid
C	cylinder
D	cuboid
E	cube
F	prism

1.

2.

3.

4.

5.

6.

7.

8.

Remember . . .

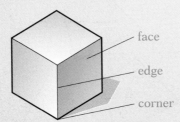

face
edge
corner

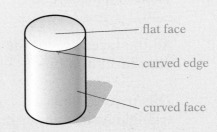

flat face
curved edge
curved face

Exercise 2   What number goes in the gap?

1. A cube has _____ faces.
2. A sphere has _____ corners.
3. A cuboid has _____ edges.
4. A cylinder has _____ flat faces and _____ curved face.
5. A cube has _____ corners.
6. A cylinder has _____ curved edges.

Sometimes we draw a solid
as a see-through shape.
We dot the edges that we
would see if it was see-through.

Exercise 3   **A**   What goes in the gap?

1. This solid is a _____ .
2. It has _____ faces.
3. It has _____ corners.
4. It has _____ edges.

B   What goes in the gap?

1. This solid is a _____ .
2. It has _____ faces.
3. It has _____ corners.
4. It has _____ edges.

C   What goes in the gap?

1. This solid is a _____ .
2. It has _____ corners.
3. It has _____ edges.
4. It has _____ curved faces.
5. It has _____ faces.

D   Which of these solids has the most faces?

1.   2.   3.

Task 1

You will need a copy of this
scissors
sticky tape

A Cut out this shape. It is called a **net**.

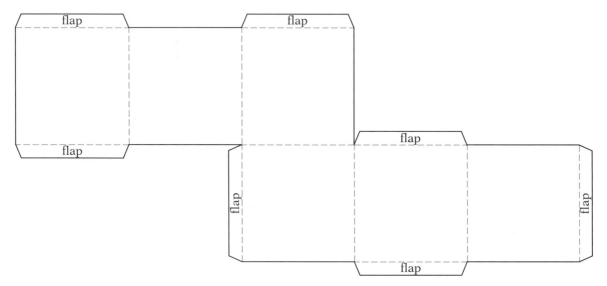

Fold it along the dashed lines to make a cube.
Tuck the flaps inside and tape them.

B Work out which of these nets can be folded to make a cube.
You may like to cut them out and test them.

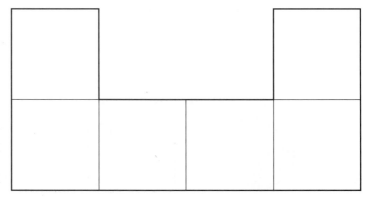

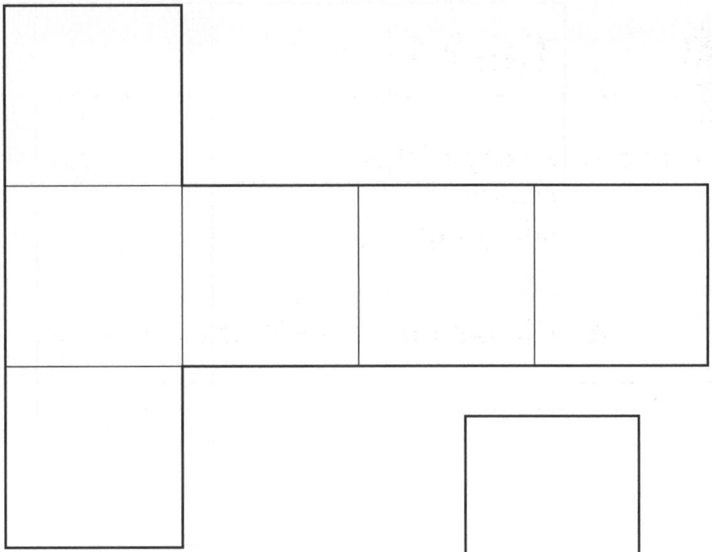

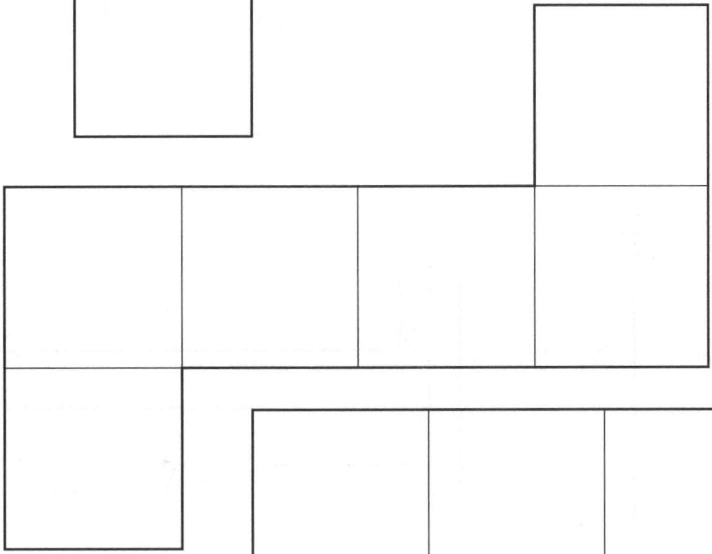

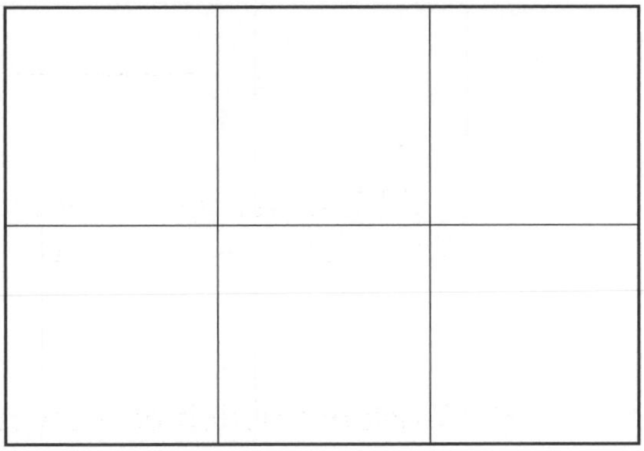

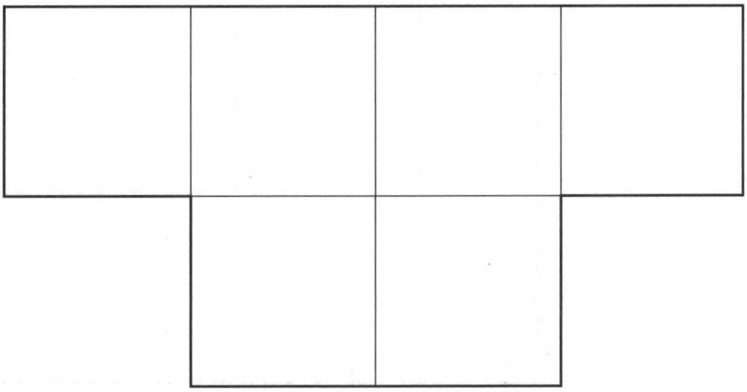

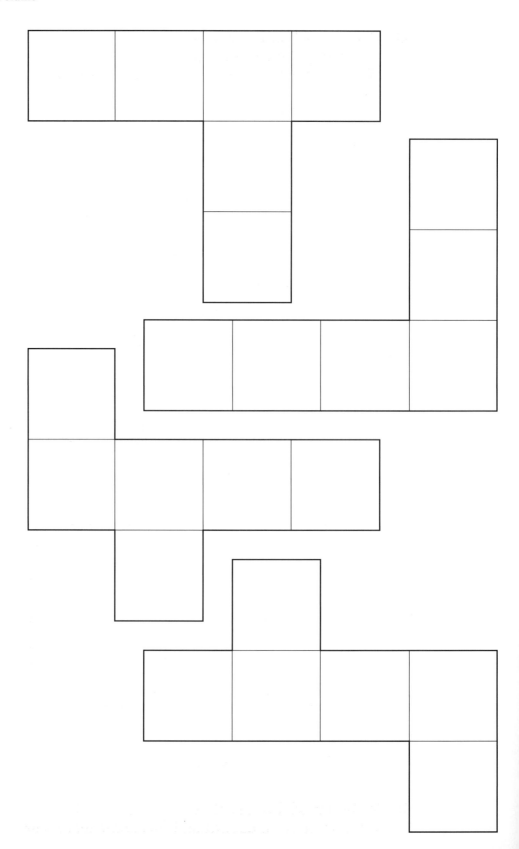

C   Cut out each of these nets.
  Fold along the dashed lines.
  Write the name of the solid you have made on it.

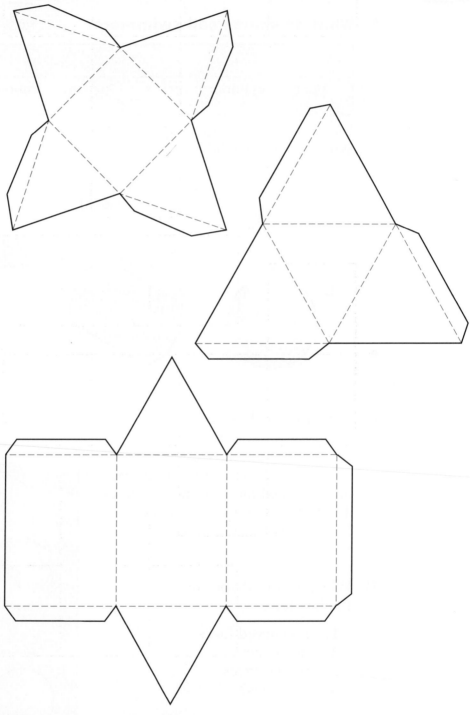

D   Make a model from solids.
  You may need to cut out and fold some more nets.

Homework/Review 1

A   **What do sharks call swimmers?**

____	__|__	____	____	____	____
sphere	cylinder	prism	prism	cuboid	pyramid

Use a copy of this box.
What are these solids called?

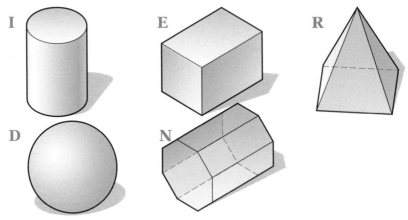

I   E   R

D   N

B   Which shape has these?
Choose from the box.
1.   5 corners, 5 faces, 8 edges
2.   1 curved face and 2 flat faces
3.   1 curved face and no flat faces
4.   5 faces, 6 corners, 9 edges
5.   6 faces, 12 edges, 8 corners

C   Which of the shapes in
the box have

1.   no curved faces
2.   no corners
3.   no flat faces
4.   no edges?

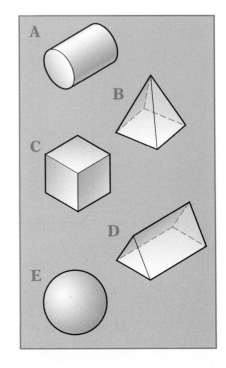

A

B

C

D

E

Volume

Volume is the amount of space
that is inside something.
The volume of the crate is
bigger than the volume of the box.

Exercise 4

1. Which of these has the biggest volume?
2. Which of these has the smallest volume?

A   B   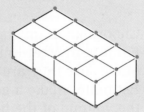   C   D

We can measure volume using cubes.

Example   The volume of this
block is 8 cubes.

Exercise 5   What is the volume of these blocks?

1.

2.

3.

4.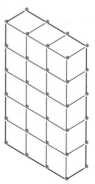

5.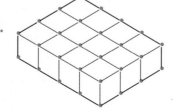

Task 2

You will need   some Multilink cubes
                some empty boxes

A Make some blocks with
       Multilink cubes.
       Find the volume of each by
       counting the number of cubes.
       Make some blocks and ask
       someone else to find the
       volume of them.

B Make a block that has a volume of 12 cubes.
       Make blocks with these volumes.
       18 cubes   24 cubes   30 cubes

C Choose an empty box.
       Fill it with Multilink cubes.
       Make sure they are stacked neatly.
       Estimate (make a good guess)
       the volume of the box.
       Get someone else to estimate
       the volume of the same box.
       Did you get the same answer?

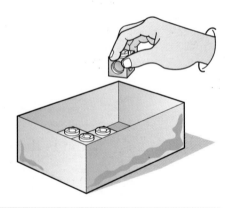

Sometimes we can't see all of the cubes.
We have to count the cubes we can't see as well.

Example   This block has 16 cubes
          on the top layer.
          It must also
          have 16 cubes
          on its bottom
          layer. (We can't
          see them all.)
          The volume of this
          block is 32 cubes.

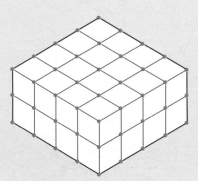

Exercise 6   **A** What is the volume of these blocks?

1.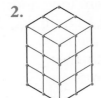

2.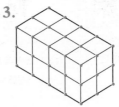

3.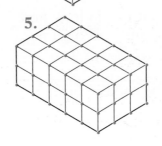

4.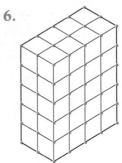

5.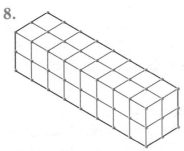

6.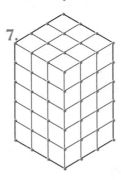

7.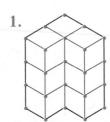

8.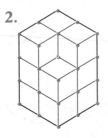

B What is the volume of these solids?

1.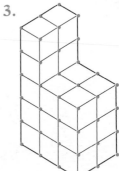

2.

3.

4.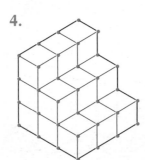

5.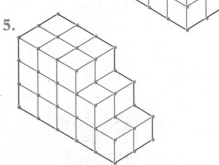

This cube is 1 cm long and
1 cm wide and 1 cm high.
We say its volume is
one cubic centimetre.
We write this as **1 cm³**.

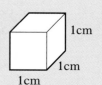

A cube that is 1 m long and
1 m wide and 1 m high is
one cubic metre or **1 m³**.

Example   Each cube used to build
this shape is 1 cm³.
It is made from
12 cubes.
The volume of the
shape is 12 cm³.

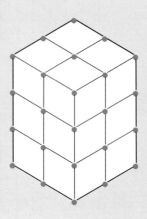

Exercise 7   Each cube used to build these shapes is 1 cm³.
Write the volume of each shape in cm³.

1.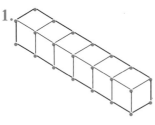

2.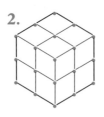

3.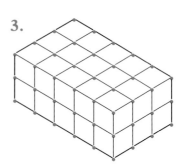

4.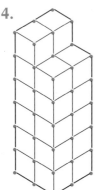

5.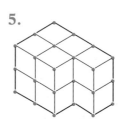

6.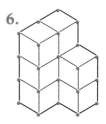

Exercise 8   **A**   Chris is putting dice into a box.
He packs the bottom layer.
He fits 4 dice across one way
and 5 dice across the other.

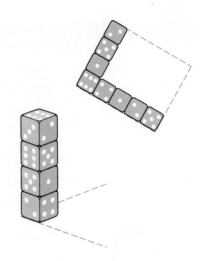

1. How many dice will
   fit on the bottom layer?

2. The box holds 4 layers exactly.
   How many dice will
   fit in the box altogether?

3. Each dice is 1 cm³.
   What is the volume of the box?

B   Selma is putting boxes of teddies on a trolley.
The bottom layer holds 3 across
one way and 2 across the other.

1. How many boxes will
   fit on the bottom layer?

2. The trolley holds
   2 layers exactly.
   How many boxes of teddies
   will it hold altogether?

3. Each box is 1 m³.
   What is the volume of the trolley?

C   Shana is stacking crates in piles.

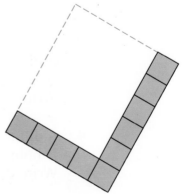

1. She makes the bottom
   layer 5 crates wide
   and 6 crates long.
   How many crates are
   on the bottom layer?

2. She stacks them
   3 crates high.
   How many crates are
   there altogether in 1 pile?

3. Each crate is 1 m³.
   What is the volume of each pile?

D   Jan was packing cubes of
bubble bath into boxes.

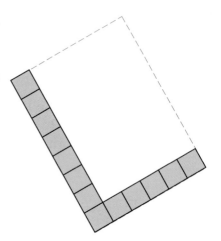

1. The bottom layer holds 8 cubes
    across one way and 6 cubes
    across the other.
    How many cubes will fit on the
    bottom layer?

2. The box holds 4 layers of cubes
    exactly.
    How many cubes will the box
    hold altogether?

3. Each cube is 1 cm³.
    What is the volume of the box?

E 1. A different box holds 32 bubble bath cubes.
        It holds 2 layers of cubes.
        One way the bottom layer could
        be filled is 8 across one way and
        2 across the other.
        How else could this layer be filled?

2. A different box holds 24 bubble bath
    cubes.
    It holds 2 layers of cubes.
    The bottom layer could be filled
    with 6 across one way and 2 across
    the other.
    How else could it be filled?

3. A different box holds 48 bubble bath cubes.
    It holds 2 layers of cubes.
    Write down 2 ways the bottom layer could be filled.

4. A different box holds 36 bubble bath cubes.
    It holds 3 layers of cubes.
    Write down 2 ways the bottom layer could be filled.

Homework/Review 2

A What is the volume of these shapes?
Give your answers in cubes.

1.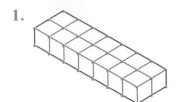

2.

3.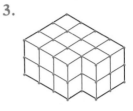

B Each cube used to build these shapes is 1 cm³.
What is the volume of each shape in cm³?

1.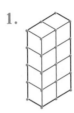

2.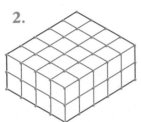

3.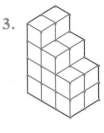

C Dan is stacking 1 cm³
cubes into a box.

1. The bottom layer holds
   7 cubes across one way
   and 5 across the other.
   How many cubes will fit on
   the bottom layer?

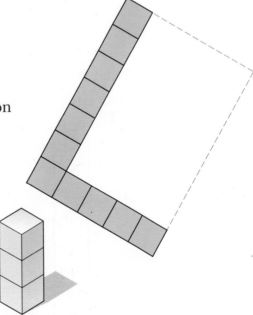

2. The box holds exactly
   3 layers of cubes.
   How many cubes does
   the box hold altogether?

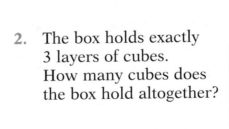

3. What is the volume of the box?

◀◀ CHAPTER REVIEW ◀◀

◀◀
Exercise 1
on page 308

A Name each of these solids.

1.

2.

3.

4.

5.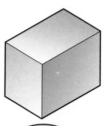

6.

◀◀
Exercise 3
on page 309

B What goes in the gap?

1. This solid is a _____ .
2. It has _____ faces.
3. It has _____ edges.
4. It has _____ corners.

◀◀
Exercises 5
and 6 on
pages 315
and 317

C What is the volume of these?
Give your answers in cubes.

1.

2.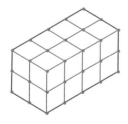

3.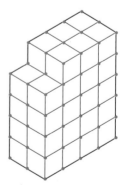

Exercise 7
on page 318

D Each cube used to build these solids is 1 cm³.
Write the volume of each in cm³.

1.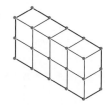

2.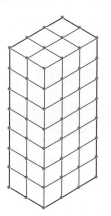

3.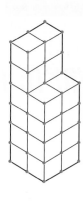

Exercise 8
on page 319

E Wendy is putting sugar
cubes into a box.

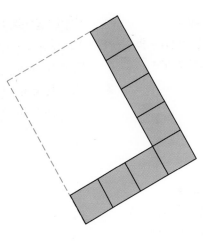

1. On the bottom layer
    she fits 4 across one
    way and 5 across the other.
    How many sugar cubes
    will fit on the bottom layer?

2. The box holds exactly 6 layers.
    How many sugar cubes
    will fit in the box altogether?

3. Each sugar cube is 1 cm³.
    What is the volume of the box?

4. Wendy packs the sugar cubes into a different box.
    It holds exactly 24 cubes.
    Wendy packs them in 2 layers.
    Write down 3 ways she could have packed the bottom layer.

Probability

Will it happen?..............................

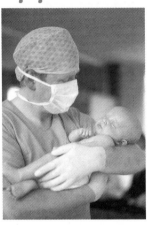

Which of the following **will happen**?
Which **might happen**?
Which **will** *not* **happen**?

• A baby will be born somewhere tomorrow.
• If you roll a dice you will get a six.
• A pig will fly past your window.
• The sun will rise tomorrow.
• It will rain tomorrow.
• You will go to school next Sunday.
• You will see a bird today.
• A cat will have puppies tomorrow.
• You will blink soon.

How likely

	Some events are **certain** to happen.
Examples	Someone in the world will die tomorrow. If you go to the library you will see a book.
	Some events are **impossible** and will not happen.
Examples	You will see a flying cow. It will rain every day for 2 years.

Some events **might** happen.

Examples   It will rain next Saturday.

Someone in your class will be sick tomorrow.

Exercise 1   Write **might happen**, **will happen** or
will not happen for each of these.

1. You will turn into a bee tomorrow.

2. A plane will fly somewhere tomorrow.

3. It will be sunny next Monday.

4. Your hair will turn green while you are asleep.

5. The next person to walk past the school gate will be a boy.

6. The next teacher you see will be smiling.

7. You will see a bird in the next year.

8. If you roll a dice, you will get a 4.

9. If you roll a dice, you will get a 9.

10. If you pick a card from a pack of cards you will get a heart.

We use these words to say **how likely** an event is to happen.

> **very likely**
>
> **likely**
>
> **unlikely**
>
> **very unlikely**

Examples   It is **very unlikely** you will fly to the moon before you die.

It is **very likely** you will use the phone next year.

Exercise 2

A   Write **likely** or **unlikely** for each of these.

1.   You will have tea tonight.

2.   This spinner will
     stop on blue.

3.   It will rain next month.

4.   Someone in your class
     will be a movie star.

5.   You will get a number
     bigger than 2 if you roll a dice.

6.   You will be able to see the stars one night next week.

B   Write **certain**, **likely**, **unlikely** or **impossible** for each of these.

1.   The next family you meet will have
     4 girls.

2.   The next car you see will have
     4 doors.

3.   School will be open on
     Christmas Day.

4.   The next lorry you see will be pink.

5.   The next time you roll a dice you
     will get a 6.

6.   The next car you see driving along the road will have wheels.

7.   The day after Tuesday will be Saturday.

8.   It will be cold on Christmas Day.

9.   Someone in your class will eat
     bread tomorrow.

10. This spinner will stop on blue.

C Bik and Sue are playing a game.

| 8 | 5 | 3 | 9 | 1 | 4 | 7 |

Bik has these cards in her hand.
Sue takes one of Bik's cards without looking.

What word goes in the gap?
Choose from the box.

| impossible |
| not likely |
| likely |
| certain |

1. It is _____ that Sue's card
    will be less than 10.

2. It is _____ that Sue's card
    will be an even number.

3. It is _____ that Sue's card will have the number 12 on it.

4. It is _____ that Sue's card will be less than 8.

D Tess and Dot are playing a game with this spinner.

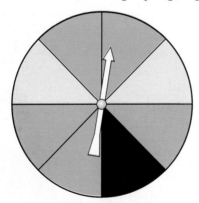

Tess spins the spinner.

What word goes in the gap?
Choose from the box.

| impossible |
| not likely |
| likely |
| certain |

1. It is _____ that the spinner will
    stop on blue.

2. It is _____ that the spinner will
    stop on red.

3. It is _____ that the spinner will stop on blue, grey
    or black.

4. It is _____ that the spinner will stop on grey.

Task

4 piles of different coloured counters
a bag

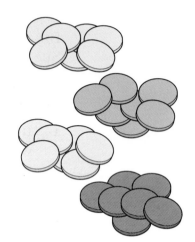

A   Put 4 of one colour and
        1 of another colour in the bag.

   1.   Pull out 1 counter without looking.

   2.   Write down what colour it is.

   3.   Put it back.

Do these 3 steps 10 more times.
Which colour did you get most of?
Explain why this was.

B   Put 10 of one colour and
        9 of another colour and
        1 of another colour in the bag.

Do the 3 steps in **A** 17 times.
Which colour did you get most of?
Which colour did you get next most of?
Explain why this was.

C   **1.**   Put two colours of counter in the bag so that it is more likely
        you will get one colour than the other if you take one.
        Test by doing the 3 steps in **A** 20 times.

   2.   Put three colours of counter in the bag so that it is more
        likely you will get one colour than either of the other ones.
        Test by doing the 3 steps in **A** 20 times.

Some events are **more** likely to happen than others.

Example   It is more likely this
spinner will stop on
blue than on white.

This is because the
blue part is bigger
than the white part.

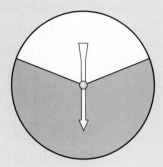

Jan puts these in a bag.

She takes out 1 counter without looking.
It is less likely to be light blue
than dark blue.

Exercise 3   **A**   1.   Lisa puts these shapes in a bag.

She takes a shape without looking.
Which shape is it more likely to be?

2.   Bill puts these shapes in a bag.

He takes one without looking.
Which shape is it more likely to be?

B   Which colour are these spinners less likely to stop on?

1.   2.   3.   4.

C

1. Caryl takes a card without looking.
   Is she more likely to get a ◯ or a △ ?

2. Is Caryl's card more likely to have an odd or an even number on it?

3. Caryl mixes the cards up and turns them face down.

③

She turns one over. It has ③ on it.
She turns another card over.
Is it more likely she will get a number smaller than 6 or a number bigger than 6?

D 1. Bev chooses a balloon from Stand A without looking.

   Which colour is she more likely to get?

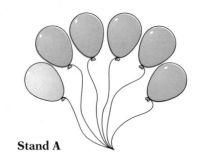

Stand A

2. Mick chooses a balloon from Stand B without looking. Which colour is he more likely to get?

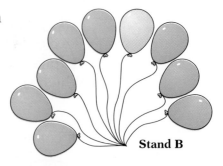

Stand B

3. Sam wanted a blue balloon.
   Is he more likely to get a blue balloon from Stand A or Stand B?

Sometimes we have to choose the **most likely** or **least likely** event.

Example

Pam took a card without looking.

It is **most likely** to have a cat on it.
It is **least likely** to have a rabbit on it.

Why is this?

Exercise 4   **A** These counters were put in a bag.

Sue took 1 counter without looking.

1. What colour is she most likely to get?
    Explain why.

2. What colour is she least likely to get?
    Explain why.

B What colour is the spinner most likely to stop on?

1. 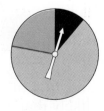   2. 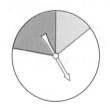   3.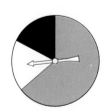

4. 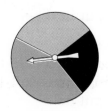   5. 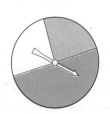   6.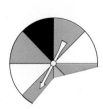

C Tim and Nesta are making up a game.
You drop a 10 p coin onto the board.
If it lands on a blue square you win.

These are the boards they made up.

 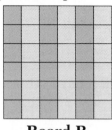 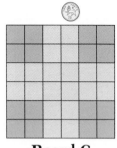

Board A   **Board B**   **Board C**

1. Which board are you most likely to win on?
   Explain why.

2. Which board are you least likely to win on?
   Explain why.

D Tandy had 3 packets of sweets.

 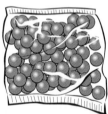 

toffees   **blackballs**   **mints**

1.

   She put these 7 sweets into a bag.

   Her friend took one without looking.
   Which sweet was she most likely to get?

2. When the bag was empty Tandy put in some more sweets.
   She wanted to make it less likely that a blackball would be
   taken than a toffee.
   What sweets could Tandy put into her bag?

3. Her friend liked toffees best.
   She asked Tandy to put some sweets in the bag that would
   make it most likely she would choose a toffee.
   What sweets could Tandy put in?

Examples   This table shows what ice-creams
            were sold at lunch time.
            Ellen saw someone with an ice-cream.

chocolate	25
vanilla	10
orange	6
caramel	15

1. What kind is it most likely to be?

2. What kind is it least likely to be?

Answers   1. It is most likely to be chocolate because there were more
               chocolate sold than any other kind.

2. It is least likely to be orange because there were less orange
    sold than any other kind.

Exercise 5   A   This table shows the colour of bears
                   won at a fun park.
                   Sam saw someone holding a bear.

blue	16
pink	10
red	21
green	6

1. What colour is it most likely to be?

2. What colour is it least likely to be?

B   This table shows the types of pies
     sold at Sports Day.
     Mrs. Chen saw someone eating a pie.

mince	18
chicken	12
bacon	6
apple	14

1. What type is it most likely to be?

2. What type is it least likely to be?

C   This table shows the colour of
     sweets in a bag.
     I take a sweet without looking.

red	23
green	16
yellow	5
blue	3
orange	19

1. What colour sweet am I most
    likely to get?
    Say why.

2. What colour sweet am I least likely to get?
    Say why.

D   Ann put 20 counters in a bag.
She takes one out without looking.
She writes down its colour.
She puts it back in the bag.
She does this 20 times.
The table shows what colours she got.

red	4
green	8
blue	3
yellow	2
white	3

1.   She pulled out 4 red counters.
Does this mean there are 4 red counters in the bag?
Explain your answer.

2.   Could there be any orange counters in the bag?
Explain your answer.

3.   She takes another counter out without looking.
What colour is it most likely to be?

E   Bill put 30 cards in a bag.
He takes one out without looking.
He writes down the shape on it.
He puts it back.
He does this 30 times.
The table shows what shapes he got.

◇	7
♡	10
☐	6
⏢	4
◯	3

1.   He pulled out 6 cards with ☐ on them.
Does this mean there are 6 cards in the bag with ☐ on them?
Explain.

2.   What is the smallest number of cards that could have a ♡
on them?

3.   Bill had put one card in the bag with a ⌂ on it.
Why is it not on the table?

4.   Bill gave the bag of cards to Colin.
Colin pulled out one card without looking.
What shape is most likely to be on the card?
Explain your answer.

Homework/Review 1

A Ama and Owen play a card game.
These cards are in a pile.

| 1 | 3 | 6 | 2 | 7 | 9 | 5 | 11 | 4 |

Owen picks a card without looking.
What word goes in the gap?
Choose from the box.

> **impossible**
>
> **not likely**
>
> **likely**
>
> **certain**

1. It is _____ that Owen's card
   will be blue.

2. It is _____ that Owen's card
   will be red.

3. It is _____ that Owen's card
   will have an even number on it.

4. It is _____ that Owen's card will have a number
   less than 12 on it.

B Gwen chose one of these cards without looking.

1. Which shape is she most likely to get?
2. Which shape is she least likely to get?
3. Gwen mixes the cards up and puts them face down.

   She turns one over.
   Is the next card she turns over more likely to be

   ◇ or ▢ ?

4. Gwen wanted to put some cards in a pile so that it was more

   likely she would choose a ◎ than a ◇ .

   What cards could she put in the pile?
   Explain your answer.

C This table shows the number of sweets in a packet.

red	18
green	12
blue	6
yellow	21

I take a sweet without looking.

1. Which colour am I most likely to take out?
   Say why.

2. Which colour am I least likely to take out?
   Say why.

Evens

Some events have an **even** chance of happening.
This means they have as much chance of happening as they have of not happening.

Examples　Getting a head when a coin is tossed.
Getting a red card when a card is taken from a pack of playing cards.

Exercise 6　Do these events have an even chance of happening?

1. The next baby born will be a boy.

2. Sam will get a 6 when he tosses a dice.

3. Sam will get an even number when he tosses a dice.

4. When Sam chooses one of these cards without looking he will get a 3.

5. This spinner will stop on blue.

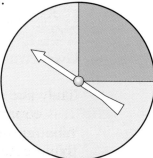

Some events have the same chance of happening as other events.
We say they have **equal chance** of happening or they are **equally likely**.

Example   When we toss a dice we have an equal chance of getting a 1, 2, 3, 4, 5 or 6.

Exercise 7

1. Mick plays a game with this spinner.
   He thinks he has an equal chance of getting green or blue.
   Is Mick right?
   Explain your answer.

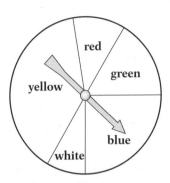

2. Kelly plays a game with this spinner.
   She thinks she has an equal chance of getting grey or blue.
   Is she right?
   Explain your answer.

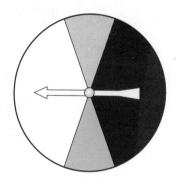

3. Mick and Kelly play a game with counters.
   They have piles of blue, black and grey counters.

   They put some counters in a bag.
   It is **equally likely** they will pick a grey or a black or a blue counter.
   What counters might they have put in the bag?

Fair and unfair

When everyone in a game has an **equal chance** of winning, the game is **fair**.

Game for a class: LAST OUT

You will need   a spinner like this with counters that match the colours on the spinner

To play
- Put the same number of each colour counter in a bag.
- Take one counter without looking.
- Your teacher spins the spinner.
- If the spinner stops on the colour which is the same as your counter, you are out.
- The last person out is the winner.

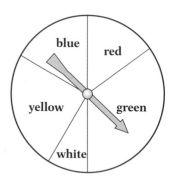

The game you have just played is *not* fair.

Why not?

How could you make it fair?

Exercise 8   **A**   Would it be a fair game if LAST OUT was played with these spinners?

1.

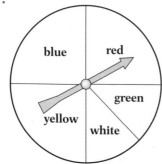

2.

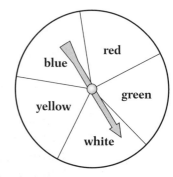

3.

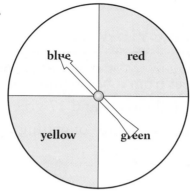

4.

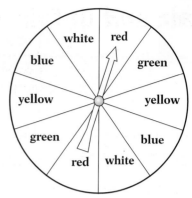

B   Sara, Viv and Ravi play a game called TOSS 6.
The first to toss 6 ten times wins.
They have 3 different cubes.

Sara's cube has the
numbers 4, 4, 4, 6, 6, 6

Viv's cube has the
numbers 6, 3, 4, 1, 1, 2

Ravi's cube has the
numbers 5, 6, 6, 3, 4, 2

1.   Is this a fair game?
2.   Who is most likely to win?
3.   Who is least likely to win?
4.   How could you make this game fair?

C

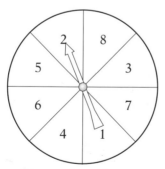

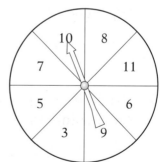

Emma's spinner   Paul's spinner

Emma and Paul made up a game.

They each spin their spinner 10 times.
They add up the 10 numbers they get.
The person with the biggest total wins.
1.   Is this a fair game?
Explain your answer.
2.   Who is most likely to win?

Homework/Review 2

A 1. Deri took a sweet from a bag without looking.
The bag had 17 red sweets and 17 green sweets.
Did he have an even chance of getting a red sweet?

2. The names of 16 cats and
12 dogs are put in a hat.

One name is taken out
without looking.

Is there an even chance
it will be a dog?

B Mick and Kelly play a game with cubes.
4 red, 8 green and 6 blue cubes are put in a bag.

1. Mick takes a cube without looking.
Does he have an equal chance of getting green or blue?

2. What extra cubes would they need to put in the bag to make
it equally likely they would get a red or a green or a
blue cube?

C Penny and Rose made up a game.
They took turns to roll a dice.
Each added the numbers they got.
The first to get to 30 was the winner.
One rule was this.

If Penny rolls a 6 she gets another turn.

If Rose rolls a 1 or a 2 she gets another turn.

1. Is this game fair?

2. Who is more likely to win?

3. How could you make it fair?

◀◀ CHAPTER REVIEW ◀◀

Exercise 2
on page 326

A Adam and Julie are playing a game with this spinner.

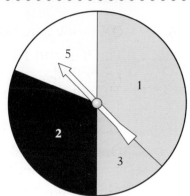

Adam spins the spinner.
Which of the words from the box go in the gap?

impossible	not likely	likely	certain

1. It is _____ that the spinner will stop on an odd number.

2. It is _____ that the spinner will stop on grey.

3. It is _____ that the spinner will stop on red.

4. It is _____ that the spinner will stop on a number less than 10.

Exercise 3
on page 329

B 1. Don put these discs in a bag.

He chooses one without looking.
Is he more likely to get a blue or a grey disc?

2. Brenda put these discs in a bag.

She chooses one without looking.
Is she more likely to get an odd or an even number?

3. Sita wants a blue disc.
Is she more likely to get a blue disc from Don's or Brenda's bag?

4. Tom wants a disc with an odd number.
Is he more likely to get this from Don's or Brenda's bag?

◄◄ Exercises 4 and 6 on pages 331 and 336

C Fred had 3 kinds of fruit.

apples   **oranges**   **peaches**

1. He put these 8 in a bag.

He put his hand in the bag and took one without looking.
What kind of fruit is he most likely to get?

2. Fred puts fruit in another bag.
What fruit could he put in the bag so that it is most likely he will choose a peach?

3. He put 3 apples and 3 oranges in a bag.
Does he have an even chance of choosing an apple?

◄◄ Exercise 5 on page 333

D This table shows the colour eyes of the people at Kim's school.
I walk around the school.

blue	68
brown	94
green	18
hazel	37

1. What colour eyes is the first person I see most likely to have?

2. What colour eyes is the first person I see least likely to have?

◄◄ Exercise 7 on page 337

E Tan played a game with this spinner.
He thinks he has an equal chance
of getting blue or red.
Is Tan right?
Explain your answer.

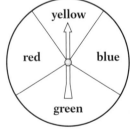

◄◄ Exercise 8 on page 338

F A rule in a game played with dice is this.

If Player A rolls a 1 or a 2, both players add 10 to their points.

If Player B rolls a 1 or a 2, this player adds 10 to his or her points.

1. Is this game fair?

2. Who is more likely to win?

3. How could you make it fair?

Quick Test 8 ✗

A Linda worked in a chocolate factory.
She worked out the number of dark
chocolates in a box like this.
Multiply the number of white chocolates
in the box by 3 then add 2.
How many dark chocolates are there in a box if there are

1. 3 white chocolates
2. 4 white chocolates
3. 6 white chocolates
4. 10 white chocolates?

B At Christmas, boxes of chocolates had strips of glitter put on them.

Box 1   **Box 2**   **Box 3**

4 strips   **8 strips**   **12 strips**

1. What are the missing numbers on this table?

Box number	1	2	3	4
Number of strips of glitter	4	8	___	___

2. What rule goes in the box?

Box number → [Rule] → Number of strips of glitter

3. Finish this rule.
   Number of strips of glitter = Box number × _____ .

C The chocolates come in all different shaped boxes.
Name each of these solid shapes.

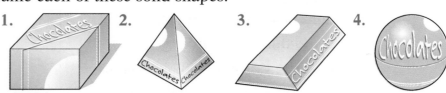

1.   2.   3.   4.

D Cubes of chocolate were made for a display.
Each cube is 1 cm³.
What is the volume of these?

1.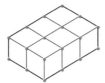
2.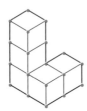
3.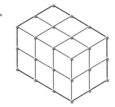

E The cubes are packed in boxes.

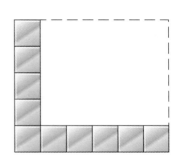

1. 5 cubes fit across one way and
   6 across the other on the bottom layer.
   How many cubes will fit on this layer?

2. The box holds exactly 5 layers.
   How many cubes will fit in a box?

3. What is the volume of each box?

F These chocolates are in a box.

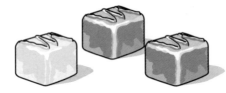

1. Linda chooses one without looking.
   Is she more likely to get a square or round chocolate?

2. Linda thinks she is more likely to get a dark chocolate.
   Explain why Linda is wrong.

3. Linda wants a white chocolate.
   What chocolates could she add to the box to make it more
   likely she would get a white one?

G The factory staff play games at Christmas.
Team A try and throw counters
onto the blue part.
Team B try and throw counters
onto the grey part.
Each time a counter lands in the
right place, the team gets a point.

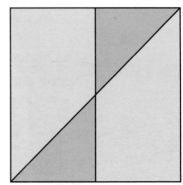

1. Is this game fair?

2. Who is more likely to win?

3. How could you make it fair?